ENHANCED SOUND

22 Electronics Projects For The Audiophile

To Susan, who cooked, and to Angel, who built every project.

ENHANCED SOUND

22 Electronics Projects For The Audiophile

Richard Kaufman

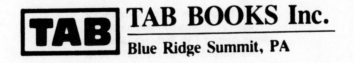

TAB BOOKS Inc.

Blue Ridge Summit, PA

FIRST EDITION
FIRST PRINTING

Copyright © 1988 by TAB BOOKS Inc.
Printed in the United States of America

Library of Congress Cataloging in Publication Data

Kaufman, Richard (Richard Joseph), 1945-
Enhanced sound—22 electronic projects for the
audiophile.

Includes index.
1. High-fidelity sound systems—Amateurs' manuals.
I. Title. II. Title: Enhanced sound—twenty-two
electronics projects for the audiophile.
TK9968.K38 1988   621.389'332   88-12366

ISBN 0-8306-9017-4
ISBN 0-8306-9317-3 (pbk.)

Questions regarding the content of this book
should be addressed to:

Reader Inquiry Branch
TAB BOOKS Inc.
Blue Ridge Summit, PA 17294-0214

TAB BOOKS Inc. offers software for
sale. For information and a catalog,
please contact TAB Software Department,
Blue Ridge Summit, PA 17294-0850.

Contents

Introduction

THE FOUNDER OF OUR LOCAL AUDIO SOCIETY ONCE SAID "THERE ARE THREE KINDS OF audiophile—those who measure, those who build, and those who listen." To this I would add that those of us who build do it because we can get better sound for less money than those who only listen. Because you are reading this, it's a safe bet that you are one who likes to build. Many of these projects have no commercial equivalents, so your system can be better in some respects than anything money alone can buy.

Rather than presenting a project as a series of steps to be followed to build a specific device, general principles will be emphasized so that you will be able to tailor each project to your own needs. No etching of circuit boards is necessary. Pre-etched IC boards, available at Radio Shack, can be used where boards are required.

It helps if you have built at least one Heathkit or Haffler, or some similar kit. If not, Chapters 1-3 will cover such basics as how to prepare circuit boards, select and recognize components, and how to solder. Simple circuits will follow, including the major prerequisite for any project, the power supply. A number of novel circuits using op amps are shown, as well as many active filter circuits for crossovers and noise reduction. No audio system would be complete without a pre-amp and amplifier, and these too are covered. Several antennas are presented for FM reception. If you have FM reception problems, and everyone else in your area also seems to have them, one of these should improve things tremendously. A set of computer programs that I developed to design my own speakers is presented and explained, although no attempt is made to describe a specific speaker construction project.

The first chapters are concerned with basic principles. The more experienced reader will wish to skip ahead to more advanced topics. In doing so, you will be following Samuel Johnson's advice: Dr. Johnson once told his biographer, James Boswell, that the proper way to read a book is to start wherever one likes, and read through it in whatever order one's interests dictate. In this way the reader will not grow bored, but will find some facet of the book that will interest him. Curiosity will lead him to backtrack, filling in any gaps in his knowledge as they become evident. Happy reading.

1

Introduction to Electronic Construction: Basic Components

THE BASIC ELECTRONIC COMPONENTS ARE THE RESISTOR, THE CAPACITOR, AND THE inductor. These are "passive" components, which do not produce a gain in voltage. "Active" components, by contrast, produce gain, that is, they can amplify a signal. The vacuum tube and transistor are components of this type. Integrated circuits are chips that contain hundreds, sometimes thousands, of these components. Some, such as operational amplifiers, or op amps, are classed as linear devices. It is with these, as opposed to digital devices, that this text will be concerned.

————————————RESISTORS————————————

Resistors provide the R in Ohm's law:

$$R = E/I$$

The resistance in a circuit is equal to E, the electromotive force, or voltage, divided by I, the current. Change the resistance, and the voltage and/or the current in the circuit must change. The total resistance of resistors in series is the sum of their individual resistances. (*Series* resistors are end-to-end, so each electron must flow through both resistors, one after the other. *Parallel* resistors are side-by-side, like railroad ties. Some electrons flow through one, some through the other, meeting up again where the resistors are joined on the other end.) In parallel, the resistance is given by:

1

$$R = \cfrac{1}{\cfrac{1}{R1} + \cfrac{1}{R2} + \cfrac{1}{R3} + \cfrac{1}{R4} \cdots}$$

If there are only two resistances in parallel, this formula reduces to:

$$R = \frac{R1}{R1} \times \frac{R2}{R2}$$

These formulas are useful if you need an otherwise unavailable resistance. By using series or parallel combinations, you can obtain any desired value.

Resistors are rated by power-handling ability, in watts, and by resistance, in ohms, and by percentage accuracy. The most common resistors were once ½ and ¼ watt, but ⅛ watt is increasingly common, and more than adequate for modern circuits which don't draw much current. Five percent resistors are readily available and are accurate enough for most applications. Some filter circuits require 1% accuracy. As of this writing, Radio Shack has begun carrying 1% resistors in the most common sizes. This makes material procurement easier for the project builder.

There are several types of resistor: wirewound, carbon composition, carbon film, cermet film, and metal film. Wirewound resistors consist of a resistive wire such as nichrome, wound about an insulated core. They are more costly than other types, and tend to behave like an inductor at higher frequencies. They are best suited for high power requirements. Carbon composition are the least costly. They are made of a solid cylinder composed of a mixture of carbon and nonconductive material enclosed in an insulated jacket with wire leads attached at either end. By changing the ratio of carbon powder to inert filler, different resistance values can be obtained. Wattage ratings range from ⅛ to 2 W. Resistance accuracy can be maintained to within 10% during manufacture. Five percent accuracy is obtained using automatic sorting equipment. For most purposes, carbon composition is acceptable, but the lack of precision, and a tendency to change value excessively with temperature changes, makes them undesireable for active filters and applications requiring close tolerances.

Film resistors are made by depositing a thin film of a partially conducting material on an insulating substrate core. This film forms a spiral over the cylindrical substrate. The film can consist of carbon, nichrome, or a metal-ceramic glaze. The wire leads are welded to wire end caps which are fitted over the film-substrate assembly, and the whole thing is covered with an insulating coating. Metal film is most widely used for precision applications, and tolerances as low as 0.1% are available, though 1% is normal. Cermet film resistors, a ceramic-metal combination, are available in 1% accuracy. They change value with aging more than metal film, but are good enough for any project in this book. Carbon film resistors are available in 1% tolerance, though 5% is normal. They too are suited for most applications. Although changes in value with temperature and aging are greater than for cermet, they are still an order of magnitude less than for carbon composition.

Resistors are color coded with several bands, as illustrated in Fig. 1-1. The key to this code is shown in Table 1-1. If you have trouble remembering these colors, memorize the old adage: {"Bad Boys Rape Our Young Girls, But Violet Gives Willingly."}

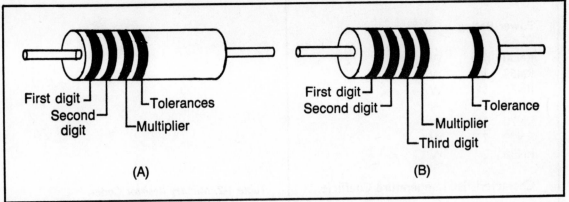

First digit ⌐
Second ⌐
digit
⌐Tolerances
⌐Multiplier

(A)

First digit ⌐
Second digit ⌐
⌐Tolerance
⌐Multiplier
⌐Third digit

(B)

Fig. 1-1. Resistor color code. (A) 5 % and 10% color code. (B) 1% color code.

The sequence of first letters is the same as the code. Twenty percent tolerance resistors have only three bands to indicate resistance; the one nearest to an end is the first digit, the next is the second digit, and the third is the multiplier. Thus green-blue-orange signifies a 56,000 ohm, ±20%, resistor. A fourth band of gold or silver indicates a five or 10% tolerance. One percent resistors will have five such bands; the first three indicate the first three significant digits, the fourth is the multiplier, and the fifth indicates the tolerance. Thus, brown-black-black-orange-brown indicates 100,000 ohms, 1% tolerance.

A military numbering system is often used for 1% resistors instead of color coding. It consists of a power rating, an optional characteristic, a value, and a tolerance code. Typically, a resistor would be labeled:

RN55 D 1023 F

Table 1-1. Standard Color Code for Resistors.

Color	Digit	Multiplier	Tolerance
Black	0	1	
Brown	1	10	1%
Red	2	100	
Orange	3	1000	
Yellow	4	10,000	
Green	5	100,000	
Blue	6	1,000,000	
Violet	7	10,000,000	
Gray	8	-	
White	9	-	
Gold	-	0.1	5%
Silver	-	-	10%

Power Rating

RN50	$\frac{1}{10}$	W
RN55	$\frac{1}{8}$	W
RN60	$\frac{1}{4}$	W
RN65	$\frac{1}{2}$	W
RN70	$\frac{3}{4}$	W
RN75	1	W
RN80	2	W

Characteristic: Temperature Coefficient

B	500 ppm/degree centigrade
C	250 ppm/degree centigrade
D	100 ppm/degree centigrade
E	75 ppm/degree centigrade
F	50 ppm/degree centigrade

Tolerance

B	0.1%
C	0.25%
D	0.5%
E	1%

Table 1-2. Military Resistor Codes.

"RN55" is the power rating, ⅛ watt. "D" is the characteristic, indicating a temperature coefficient of 100 parts per million per degree centigrade. 1023 is the value: 102 being the significant digits, 3 being the number of zeros. This resistor is 102,000 ohms. "F" indicates a 1% tolerance. Decode other values as shown in Table 1-2.

Variable Resistors

Variable resistors are also known as *potentiometers*. The resistive element can be wirewound, carbon composition (including conductive plastics), or cermet. Wirewound are best suited for high power applications, requiring more than a few watts. Cermet is the most stable, changing value least with temperature change and age.

A potentiometer has three terminals. The wiper, or center element, is the moving takeoff point that travels along the resistive element. The change in resistance might be the same for equal distances traveled anywhere by the wiper, in which case the pot has a *linear taper*. For other pots it might vary, being greater on the clockwise side of the wiper's travel; this would be a *logarithmic* or an *audio taper potentiometer*.

Where only a two-terminal, variable resistor is required instead of a voltage divider, two of the terminals will be tied together in a rheostat configuration, as shown in Fig. 1-2. If terminal three were left floating, the wiper connection would be liable to become

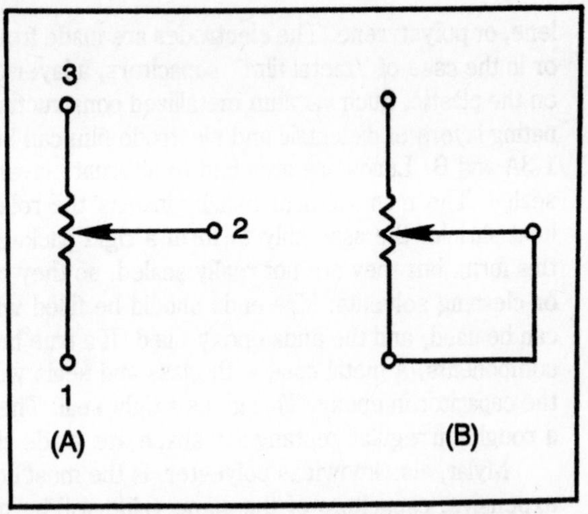

Fig. 1-2. Potentiometer connections. (A) Potentiometer. (B) Rheostat (variable resistor) configuration.

noisy with time, which is unacceptable for audio and for most other applications.

Better-quality pots are sealed to prevent dust and other airborn contaminants from causing noisy operation.

CAPACITORS

A capacitor consists of two conductors (electrodes) separated by a nonconductor, or *dielectric*. It will block a constant voltage but pass an alternating current. The efficiency with which it passes an ac current is expressed in microfarads (μF or μFd and sometimes μFd, millionths of a farad) or picofarads (pF or pFd, millionths of a microfarad). The closer a signal is to dc, the more it will be blocked by a capacitor. Generally, the bigger the capacitor, the lower the frequency it will pass. The higher the dielectric constant, the smaller a capacitor can physically be and still pass the same frequency. The total capacitance of capacitors in parallel is the sum of their individual capacitances; in series, the total capacitance is the inverse of the sum of the inverses of the individual capacitors, i.e.:

$$C = \frac{1}{\dfrac{1}{C1} + \dfrac{1}{C2} + \dfrac{1}{C3} + \dfrac{1}{C4} \cdots}$$

There is no such thing as a pure capacitor, for real-world devices also exhibit "parasitic" inductance and resistance. The dissipation factor is proportional to the effective series resistance of a capacitor; the lower it is, the better. It is primarily the nature of the dielectric material that determines the nature of the capacitor. The dielectric can be a plastic film, mica, ceramic, or an electrolytic fluid. The method of construction will greatly influence the parasitic inductance.

Film Capacitors

Film capacitors are made from a plastic film dielectric, such as mylar, polypropylene, or polystyrene. The electrodes are made from a conducting foil, usually aluminum, or in the case of "metal film" capacitors, a layer of metal is vacuum-deposited directly on the plastic. Such vacuum metallized construction is mechanically more stable. Alternating layers of dielectric and electrode film can be stacked or rolled as shown in Figs. 1-3A and B. Leads are attached to alternate layers of electrodes, and the assembly is sealed. The manufacturer usually inserts the rolled capacitor in a plastic sleeve, then heat shrinks the assembly to form a rigid package. Sometimes capacitors are sold in this form, but they are not really sealed, so they can be adversely affected by humidity or cleaning solvents. The ends should be filled with epoxy. Alternatively, a rigid tube can be used, and the ends epoxy-filled. If a true hermetic seal is needed, as for military components, a metal case with glass and seals will be used. Another method is to dip the capacitor in epoxy. This gives a tight seal. The familiar green or red capacitors with a roughly irregular rectangular shape are made this way.

Mylar, also known as polyester, is the most common of the film types and the least expensive; capacitors of the same value will be more compact than those made from other plastics. Mylar caps are available in values from .001 μF to several microfarads. They are quite acceptable in audio applications. Some audiophiles claim that polystyrene or polypropylene caps sound better in an audio circuit, but I know of no scientifically conducted test demonstrating that this is so.

Polycarbonate capacitors are larger than mylar, but show less change in value at high operating temperatures. They have a lower dissipation factor than mylar, which means they will function better in filter circuits. Polysulfone is similar to polycarbonate, but will withstand even higher temperatures, up to 150 degrees C.

Polystyrene capacitors have the best electrical properties of the plastic films. The *temperature coefficient,* or change in value with temperature, is very low, as is the dissipation factor. Maximum operating temperature is limited to 85 degrees C. They are available in values as low as a few picofarads, and as high as a microfarad or two, but the higher values are both large and expensive. Polypropylene is similar in performance, with somewhat higher dissipation and slightly greater temperature coefficient. Maximum operating temperature is 105 degrees centigrade. Cost is lower than for polystyrene, though slightly higher than for mylar.

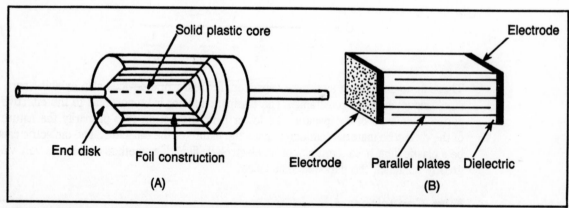

Fig. 1-3. Capacitor construction. (A) Cutaway view of film capacitor, rolled construction. (B) Stacked construction.

10	11	12	13	15	16
18	20	22	24	27	30
33	36	39	43	47	51
56	62	68	75	82	91

Table 1-3. Standard Capacitor Values.

Teflon is similar in electrical properties to polypropylene, but will operate at very high or very low temperatures. Due to its high cost, teflon is seldom encountered outside military gear, though some caps do appear on the surplus market.

Film capacitors are not usually labeled as to dielectric material, but sometimes the letters "PP," "PS," or "PC" will appear, indicating polypropylene, polystyrene, or polycarbonate. With experience, it is possible to make an educated guess as to the material, based on the capacitor's value, voltage rating, and size.

Film capacitors are available in standard values as shown in Table 1-3. Even though these values are standard, they are not all readily available to the electronics enthusiast. Fortunately, if some unavailable value is desired, other caps can be parallelled to attain a required value.

Standard tolerances range from one to 20%. Five percent is adequate for most applications.

Voltage rating is the maximum safe operating voltage for the capacitor, and is a function of the thickness of the dielectric. Most modern circuits operate at well under 100 volts, but film capacitors rated for lower voltages will often change value from the heat of a soldering iron. This is especially true of polystyrene. One hundred volts is probably safe from damage if normal construction precautions are followed.

Mica Capacitors

Silver mica capacitors are the best from an electrical standpoint, as well as being the most expensive. Dissipation and temperature coefficient are extremely low. They can operate to 150 degrees C. Values above .01 μF are not usually available, and are bulky and expensive when they are.

Construction is shown in Fig. 1-3B. Mica wafers are silvered on both sides to form electrodes, then stacked and thermally bonded. They are then dipped in epoxy resin, or for large capacitors designed to operate at high voltages, sealed in a molded plastic case. An older style of construction involved joining the plates together with rivets. Because the plates in such capacitors can move, the capacitive value is unstable.

Five percent tolerance is standard for silver mica, and one and two percent are also available.

Ceramic Capacitors

Ceramic capacitors are made using the stacked construction technique. The dielectric is a ceramic material made from barium titanate, which is cast into plates which are coated with a metallic ink, then stacked in layers and fired in ovens. The stacks are removed from the oven and cut into individual capacitors. The temperature coefficient and dielectric constant can be varied over a very wide range by the use of additives in casting the mix.

Values are available from a fraction of a picofarad to 2.2 μF. The dissipation factor is usually lower than 1%, on the same order of magnitude as mylar, and can be as low as .02%, the same as polycarbonate. Tolerance is normally 10 or 20% which limits their usefulness. They exhibit very low parasitic inductance, which makes them very useful for radio frequency (rf) work. They are not generally used in audio applications, except for rf decoupling and power-supply bypassing. Even here, some golden-eared audiophiles claim they adversely affect fidelity.

Electrolytic Capacitors

The structure of an electrolytic capacitor is shown in Fig. 1-4. It consists of two electrodes immersed in a dielectric liquid. The case is a metal can, and the leads can both be attached at one end (radial leads) or at opposite ends (axial leads). They require a polarizing voltage to operate properly. When the proper voltage is applied, the capacitor is "formed" as a dielectric oxide film is deposited on the anode, i.e., the positive electrode. This should be done as part of the manufacturing process. An aluminum electrolytic capacitor can be permanently damaged by a voltage of the wrong polarity, which can puncture the dielectric oxide film, allowing dc current to flow. Such a capacitor is said to be "leaky." Nonpolarized types are made by putting two capacitors in series, with either the plus or the minus leads connected together. Before the connection is made, the dielectric film must be formed by applying a dc voltage of the proper polarity.

Aluminum electrolytic capacitors are used in power supplies, where they are perfectly acceptable. Their use is sometimes unavoidable for passing low frequencies, but they have broad and lopsided tolerances such as +80%/−20%, they require a polarizing voltage, and have a limited shelf life. If very high capacitance is required, say several thousand μF, they are the only practical option. Large parasitic inductances and high dissipation prevent them from functioning well at high frequencies. This is why mylar or ceramic decoupling capacitors are used in power supplies—to eliminate high-frequency noise. Audiophiles claim that replacing the electrolytic output capacitors in an audio de-

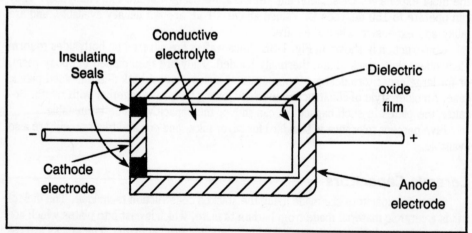

Fig. 1-4. Electrolytic capacitor construction.

vice will greatly improve the sound. This is one case where I believe the golden-ears are demonstrably right; even bypassing the electrolytic with a 1 μF plastic film capacitor will make a noticeable difference in the quality of the high frequencies. Most CD players have a 10 μF electrolytic blocking capacitor in the output signal path. If you can do this without voiding your warranty, find this capacitor by tracing the circuit back from the output jacks; solder a 1 μF plastic film bypass capacitor in parallel with the electrolytic (or replace it with at least 4 mF worth of film capacitors), and see if you can hear the difference.

For putting a large capacitance in a small space, tantalum is unequalled. Tantalum electrolytics are more rugged and have better characteristics than aluminum. They can operate without a polarizing voltage because a momentary reversal of polarity will not puncture the dielectric film. They have no shelf-life restrictions. Parasitic inductances are quite low, so they can be used at high frequencies. Dissipation is not as good as for film capacitors, being about 4%. Ten and 20% tolerances are standard. They are expensive,but pack more capacitance in less space than aluminum or plastic film. Voltage ratings are limited to below 35 V. The electrolyte can be a liquid in a metal can, or it can be saturated paper or even dry powdered tantalum, with a tantalum pentaoxide dielectric film. Dry tantalum caps are usually dip coated with epoxy, which gives them a roughly teardrop shape.

Capacitor Labeling

Although color-coding schemes similar to those used for resistors were once common and are still sometimes used, they have largely given way to the straightforward printing of voltage ratings and values on the capacitor's case.

A military code system is often used for mica capacitors; some of the codes are used for other types as well. They may be decoded using Table 1-4. Take a capacitor labeled:

CM05CD
100DO3
ARCO

"CM05" designates the case size and lead configuration. "C" is the characteristic, showing the temperature coefficient to be ±200 parts per million per degree centigrade. "D" is the dc working voltage, 500 V. "100" designates the capacitance in picofarads: 10 followed by no zero's, or 10 pF. "D" is the tolerance, ±0.5 pF. "O" shows the operating range to be −55 to +125 degrees C. "3" shows the vibration range which the capacitor will tolerate without deteriorating. "ARCO" is the manufacturer's name.

Often mica and other capacitors will be labeled similarly to one in my parts bin:

2000±5%

This is a 2000 pF (.002 μF), 5% cap. The rest is guesswork. From the size of this cap, about ¾″ × ⅜″, it is 100 V or better. A metallized polyester capacitor purchased from Radio Shack is labeled:

Characteristic

B	Not Specified	
C	+/−200	ppm/degree C
D	+/−100	ppm/degree C
E	−20 to +100	ppm/degree C
F	0 to +70	ppm/degree C

Dc Voltage

Y	50 V
A	100 V
C	300 V
D	500 V

Table 1-4. Military Capacitor Codes.

Tolerance

A	+/− 1 pF
D	+/−0.5 pF
M	+/−20%
K	+/−10%
J	+/−5%
G	+/−2%
F	+/−1%
E	+/−0.5%

Temperature Range

M	−55 to +70 degrees C
n	−55 to +85
o	−55 to +125
p	−55 to +150

.01M/250

The value is .01 μF. The decimal shows the units to be microfarads, not the "M." The "M" indicates the tolerance is 20%. However, actual measurement showed the value as .01015 μFd. The lesson here is that the rating is a "worst possible case." The actual value is sometimes much closer to the designation, but don't count on it unless you have some means of measuring.

INDUCTORS

Inductors can be thought of as the opposite of capacitors. They pass low frequencies and block high ones. They usually consist of wire coils wound about a ferric or air-filled form. Small values are available for rf work, epoxy coated or wound about a metal slug. Applications in audio are limited. Large inductors are found in the crossover networks of loudspeakers. Usually it is more economical and convenient to wind your own than to try to buy ready-made ones in these values. Low-cost equalizers sometimes use indicators, but hum pickup is a problem. Most amplifiers use a coil as part of the output network to keep operation stable at high frequencies.

This formula gives the approximate value of a single-layer air core coil:

$$L = \frac{a^2 \; n^2}{9a + 10b}$$

where

L = inductance, in microhenrys (uH)
a = coil radius, in inches
b = coil length, in inches
n = number of turns

A multilayered coil's inductance can be very roughly approximated by using the above formula to find the values for L using first the inner radius, then the outer radius, and averaging the two.

The value of inductors in series is found by adding together their individual inductances. Inductors in parallel have a value given by

$$L = \frac{1}{\dfrac{1}{L1} + \dfrac{1}{L2} + \dfrac{1}{L3} + \dfrac{1}{L4} + \cdots}$$

──INTERNATIONAL PARTS SPECIFICATION STANDARD──

The International Parts Specification Standard is used throughout the world, and is gradually gaining acceptance in this country. It avoids the unnecessary use of zeros and decimal points, and omits the symbol for ohms and the F for farad. Table 1-5 summarizes the notation in case you should encounter it.

──THE DECIBEL──

Properly speaking, the decibel (dB) is not a component, but a unit of measure. It is used to appraise signal strength in terms of relative loudness as perceived by the ear. A 40-watt signal played through a loud speaker will sound twice as loud as a 10-watt signal. This is why a 250-watt amp doesn't play twice as loud as a 100-watt one; the human ear has a logarithmic response. The number of decibels corresponding to a specific power ratio is given by the formula:

$$dB = 10 \, \log(P1/P2)$$

USA	International
2.7 k ohm	1k5
1.8 M ohm	1M8
10 μF	10μ
0.01 μF	10n
6800 pF	6n8
0.0015 μF	1n5
10 pF	10p

Table 1-5. International Parts Specification Standard.

k	=	kilo	= 10^3
M	=	mega	= 10^6
μ	=	micro	= 10^{-6}
n	=	nano	= 10^{-9}
p	=	pico	= 10^{-12}
F	=	farads	

Base 10 logarithms are used. For voltage ratios:

$$dB = 20 \log(V1/V2)$$

Table 1-6 summarizes voltage ratios for given dB units.

dB	Voltage Gain	Voltage Loss
1	1.122	.8913
2	1.259	.7943
3	1.414	.7079
4	1.585	.6310
6	1.995	.5012
10	3.162	.3162
20	10.00	.1000
30	31.62	.0316
40	100.0	.0100
60	1000	.0010
80	10000	.0001
100	100000	.00001

Table 1-6. Voltage Decibel Chart.

REFERENCES

Readers desiring further information can consult the following texts:

Williams, Arthur B. *Electronic Filter Design Handbook*. New York: McGraw-Hill Book Company, 1981.

Lancaster, Don. *Active Filter Cookbook*. Indianapolis, IN: Howard W. Sams & Co., Inc., 1979.

Staff of the American Radio Relay League. *The Radio Amateur's Handbook*. Newington, CT : The American Radio Relay League, Inc., (Updated yearly).

2

Introduction to Electronic Construction: Semiconductors

Semiconductors are the basis of modern electronics. Doing electronics without understanding how they work is like painting a picture while blindfolded. Here is a brief overview of these devices. The reader who wishes more information may explore the references given at the end of this chapter.

In insulating materials such as glass, ceramics, rubber, and most plastics, all electrons are strongly bound to the atomic nuclei. In conductors such as silver, copper, and gold, the electrons in the outer orbits about each nucleus are so loosely bound that they are shared by all the nuclei in the material. These are called *free electrons;* they are free to travel from one end of the material to the other, given the impetus of an applied voltage. Semiconductors have no free electrons, but they are not like insulators, either. The electrons are only weakly bound to the nucleus. Under the right conditions, they can be dislodged from the nucleus and behave as free electrons.

Many materials are semiconducting, but silicon is the most commonly used for transistors. The electrons in silicon are not free, and very little current will flow in pure silicon when a voltage is applied. If small amounts of antimony or arsenic are added to silicon crystals, the resulting material will have enough free electrons to conduct a substantial current. The addition of impurities to produce free electrons changes pure silicon into an n-type semiconductor. The "n" stands for "negative," because electrons are the negative charge carrier.

The absence of an electron in the outer orbit of an atom in a crystal causes the atom to be positively charged due to the positive charge inherent in the nucleus. The "hole" produced by this absence of an electron can consequently be considered to carry a positive charge equal to the charge of an electron but of the opposite sign. Holes can flow through a material just as electrons do, but they will travel in the opposite direction when a voltage is applied.

DIODES AND RECTIFIERS

A diode is formed when p and n crystals are joined, as shown in Fig. 2-1. Diodes will pass current in only one direction. If a positive voltage is applied to the anode, or p-type material, the holes will flow toward the junction. At the same time, electrons will flow through the n-type material toward the junction. When they meet at the junction, the free electrons fill the holes, and both effectively vanish. At the same time, more electrons are released into the cathode, and more holes are created at the anode, because of the applied voltage. The net result is that a current flows through the diode, which is said to be *forward biased*.

Now consider the results when a negative voltage is applied to the anode. Holes flow away from the junction, toward the negative voltage. Electrons flow away from the junction, through the n-type material. The holes and electrons do not meet at the junction, and so no charges can be exchanged. Instead, the charge carriers remain bunched up in their respective materials, away from the junction. No current can flow. The diode is *reverse biased*.

A rectifier is really the same thing as a diode. It is called a "rectifier" when used to convert alternating current to direct current. "Diode" refers to the same type of device when used to rectify or otherwise manipulate signals. The difference involves power-handling capability. Rectifiers must usually be much more rugged than diodes.

A forward-biased diode will not conduct unless the applied voltage exceeds a minimum value. For silicon, this is approximately 0.7 volts. For germanium diodes, only 0.2 volts are necessary. For this reason, germanium diodes are generally used for the detection of radio-frequency signals because they are more sensitive. Silicon will operate at higher temperatures than germanium, so it finds wide application in power supplies because the higher temperature tolerance translates into greater power-handling ability. The resistance of silicon rectifiers when reverse biased is much higher than for germanium.

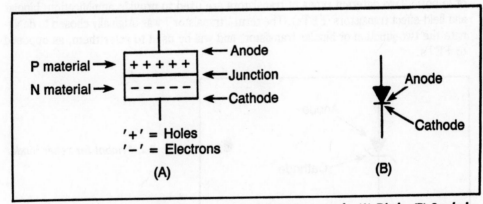

Fig. 2-1. A diode is formed by joining "p" and "n"-type crystals. (A) Diode. (B) Symbol.

The important specifications to watch when choosing rectifiers are current-handling ability and *peak inverse voltage* or *PIV*. Peak inverse voltage is the maximum voltage a reverse-biased rectifier can withstand without breaking down. The diode's destruction is usually accompanied by a visible puff of smoke. The peak voltage is 1.4 times the rms, or root-mean-square average, used to specify ac voltage. A 12-volt ac sine wave has a peak voltage of about 17 V; a 12-volt square wave, on the other hand, has a peak of 12 V. It is safest to use diodes with a PIV of at least two, and better four, times the peak voltage drop to be found in the circuit where it is used.

Zener Diodes

The zener diode is a variant which is used for voltage regulation. The symbol for a zener diode is shown in Fig. 2-2. When a diode is reverse biased, no current will flow. Increase the voltage, and at some point current will suddenly begin flowing. Usually this destroys the diode. A zener is designed to withstand such reverse biasing; as long as the current flow does not exceed the zener's rating, it will survive. However, there will be a "voltage drop" across the zener. Zeners can be designed to produce a voltage drop ranging from three to a couple of hundred volts, with power ratings from a fraction of a watt to many amps. The ability to obtain a specific voltage drop is useful in building power supplies, where the voltage must be regulated to an exact value. This topic will be covered more thoroughly in Chapter 5.

Light-Emitting Diodes

Light-emitting diodes, or LEDs, are diodes whose junctions emit photons when the diode is forward biased. They are made from gallium arsenide or gallium phosphide, or both. They are available in red, yellow, and green. Some Japanese companies have demonstrated blue LEDs, but they cannot yet be economically mass-produced. Progress in electronics being what it is, they could be available by the time these words are read.

TRANSISTORS

Transistors permit a low-level signal to control a much higher powered one. In other words, they provide a power "gain." This gain can be an increase in voltage, in current, or in both. Two different types of transistors are used to provide amplification: bipolar and field-effect transistors (FETs). The term "transistor" was originally chosen to designate the two-junction or bipolar transistor, and will be used to refer them, as opposed to FETs.

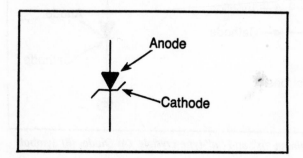

Fig. 2-2. Symbol for zener diode.

Bipolar Transistors

Bipolar transistors are made like a sandwich of n-type and p-type materials, as shown in Fig. 2-3. Transistors can be either npn or pnp, depending on the structure of the sandwich. This discussion will deal with npn transistors, but applies to pnp types by reversing all charges, and substituting holes for electrons and vice versa. Regardless of type, transistors have three elements. These are the emitter, which emits electrons, the collector, which collects them, and the base, which controls electron flow by controlling the charge concentration at the junctions.

In effect, the transistor is two np junction diodes placed back-to-back. If you apply a positive voltage to the base, so that it is forward biased, and apply a higher voltage to the collector, current will flow. Electrons leave the emitter and enter the base. Unlike a diode, the p-material in the base is relatively thin and only lightly doped, so there are not many holes to combine with electrons. Most of the electrons, about 90%, pass through the base to the collector, and so a current flows through the transistor. The current flow through the base-emitter junction determines the current flow from the collector to the emitter.

A transistor can be configured as a common emitter, common collector, or common base circuit. These are shown in Fig. 2-4. The configurations most often encountered in audio circuits are the common collector and common emitter. The ratio of the collector resistor (R_c) to the emitter resistor (R_e) determines the voltage gain of a common emitter circuit, which is approximately equal to this ratio. In fact, it is slightly less, and the maximum gain is limited by the transistor's *beta*, the measure of the base-to-collector current ratio. The common collector configuration, also called an *emitter follower*, has a voltage gain that is always slightly less than one, but its current gain is usually quite high, and so it is used in the output stage of power amplifiers.

Transistors are chosen for an application on the basis of their power dissipation ability, their frequency response, linearity, switching speed, and distortion figures, their current-handling capability, and the junction breakdown voltages, among other things. The situation is complicated by the fact that the current-handling capability is lowered when the collector-emitter voltage is raised. The manufacturer's spec sheet contains

Fig. 2-3. The bipolar transistor. (A) Npn transistor, structure and symbol. (B) Pnp transistor, structure and symbol.

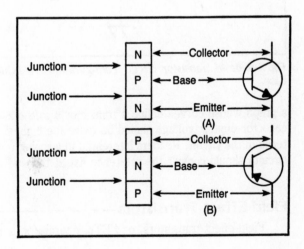

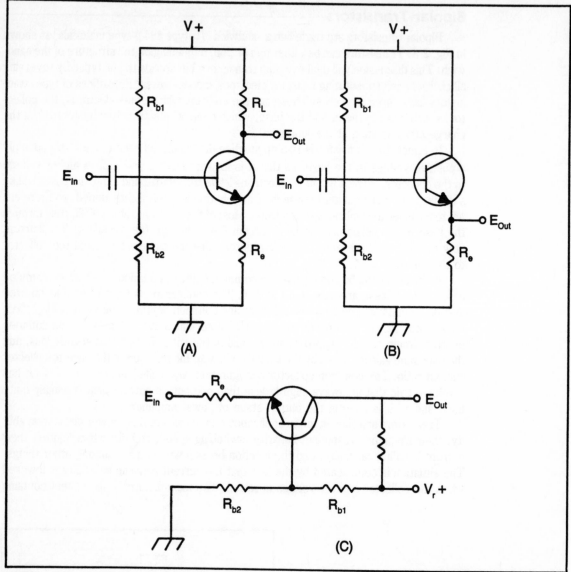

Fig. 2-4. Basic transistor circuit configurations. (A) Common emitter. (B) Common collector. (C) Common base.

a graph whose curves define a transistor's safe operating area. Usually the specified collector-emitter voltage should be twice the highest voltage difference to be encountered in the circuit. Readers interested in learning more about the design of transistor circuits should consult the reference list at the end of this chapter.

Field-Effect Transistors

Field-effect transistors, or FETs, operate on a very different principle from that of bipolars. Instead of flowing through two junctions, the current flows through a single piece of doped semiconductor (see Fig. 2-5). The connections are called the source and drain. Current flow is controlled by the voltage on the gate, a region of doped material of opposite polarity. This is significantly different from bipolar transistors, where control is applied by the base current. In this respect, FETs are more like tubes, which also control current flow by means of a voltage.

FETs can be enhancement or depletion devices, or a combination of the two. These terms refer to the fact that the gate voltage can either enhance, or deplete, the flow of electrons through the source-to-drain channel. Circuits for FETs are called common source, common drain, and common gate, and are similar to the common emitter, collector and base circuits used for bipolar devices.

A variant on the FET is the MOSFET, the metal-oxide semiconductor field-effect transistor, illustrated in Fig. 2-6. The source and drain are separated by a substrate of opposite polarity. The gate is separated from the substrate by an insulating layer of a metal oxide material. A voltage applied to the gate creates an induced channel through the substrate, allowing current to flow. The oxide layer can be punctured by too high a voltage, as from static electrical discharge, and so handling precautions are in order for these devices. Although most newer MOSFETs' gates are protected by a zener diode, they can still be destroyed by a static spark, though such a mishap is less likely. This is why MOSFET assemblers wear grounded wrist straps and build on grounded metal work benches.

FETs and MOSFETs were originally low-power devices, but trick geometries and clever chemistry have led to devices that can handle respectable amounts of power. Power MOSFETs are referred to by a variety of manufacturers' names, but MOS or FET is

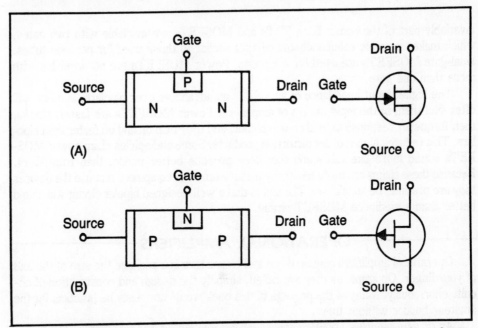

Fig. 2-5. Field effect transistors. (A) N-channel FET, structure and symbol. (B) P-channel FET, structure and symbol.

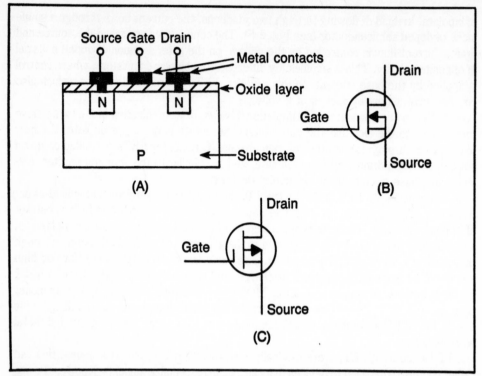

Fig. 2-6. MOSFETs. (A) Structure of n-channel MOSFET. (B) Symbol for n-channel MOSFET. (C) Symbol for p-channel MOSFET.

invariably part of the name. Both FETs and MOSFETs are available with two gates, which makes possible semiconductor circuits similar to those used for pentode tubes. Dual-gate MOSFETs are used for rf circuits. Power MOSFETs are not available with more than one gate.

The higher input impedance of an FET is an advantage over bipolars, and one will often find them in the input stages of amplifiers. Power MOSFETs are faster, that is, their frequency response extends much higher, and they turn on and off faster than bipolars. This reduces higher order distortion products. Some audiophiles claim power MOSFETs sound more like tubes, and therefore produce better music, than transistors. Because these claims are made mostly by manufacturers of equipment that use the devices they are praising, be suspicious. The fact is that a well-designed bipolar circuit will sound better than a mediocre MOSFET circuit.

OPERATIONAL AMPLIFIERS

Operational amplifiers contain dozens of transistors in a package the size of the end of your finger. Op amps, as they are called, simplify the design and construction of circuits enormously. Many of the projects in this book would not really be practical for the amateur builder without them.

An op amp requires a power supply, and has one output and two inputs. The inputs are called *differential inputs,* and are labeled "+" and "−"; a positive voltage on the positive, or noninverting input, drives the output positive, but on the negative, or inverting input, it drives the output negative. A negative voltage has the opposite effect. The op amp symbol is a triangle pointing to the one side. Several different circuits are shown in Fig. 2-7. Positive and negative inputs are on the vertical side. The opposite vertex represents the output. By convention, the output is to the right, the negative input on top, and the positive on the bottom. For convenience, or to emphasize some feature of a circuit, this convention is often violated, and the op amp may point either way.

The ideal op amp does not exist,but if it did it would have these characteristics: infinite gain, infinite input impedance, zero output impedance, zero output with no input, and a flat frequency response throughout its operating range, which would be dc to infinity. Real op amps have a maximum open loop gain (gain with no feedback element, which would lower the gain) on the order of 100 dB, which is enough for most purposes. The input impedance,though not infinite, is very high, being about a megohm for the

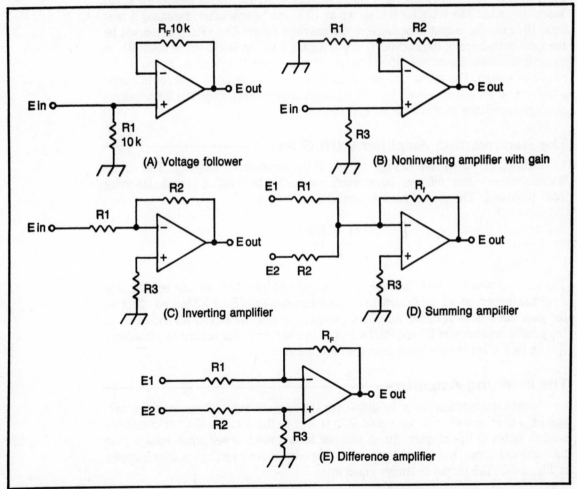

Fig. 2-7. Op amp circuit configurations. (A) Voltage follower. (B) Noninverting amplifier with gain. (C) Inverting amplifier. (D) Summing amplifier. (E) Difference amplifier.

21

741 op amp, and being a million megohms for newer devices with FET inputs, such as the LF353. A high input impedance means the device will accept input from any source, because a high impedance source can't drive a low impedance amplifier. The output impedance, though not zero, is only a few ohms, which allows the op amp to drive even amplifiers with low input impedance. With no input, an op amp will have an output of a couple of millivolts. This can be nulled out with special circuitry, or a blocking capacitor can be used. Although the frequency response of an op amp isn't flat from dc to infinity, they all are reasonably flat down to dc, and the high end response can extend to several megahertz.

The Voltage Follower

The voltage follower behaves like the emitter-follower (common collector) circuit described earlier, but without the 0.7-volt loss in signal strength the transistor circuit has. Figure 2-7A shows a practical voltage follower circuit. The output follows the input, hence the name. The value for R1, shown as 10 k, can be any value, assuming it is at least 10 times the output impedance of the previous stage. The value chosen will be the input impedance of the circuit. R_f, the feedback resistor, is chosen to equal R1, in order to minimize the output offset voltage. For noncritical application, R_f can be replaced by a short. The voltage follower is used as a buffer to isolate stages, or to enable a high-output-impedance circuit to drive a low-input-impedance amplifier; it transforms the high impedance to a low-output impedance.

The Noninverting Amplifier with Gain

Figure 2-7B shows how to vary the gain of the noninverting amplifier. This circuit is similar to the voltage follower, but an extra resistor has been added from the inverting input to ground. The gain of such an amplifier is:

$$\frac{(R1 + R2)}{R1}$$

The gain can never be less than one. (Where gains of less than one are needed, use a voltage divider, as will be illustrated by the difference amplifier.) R3 has no effect on the gain, but it does influence the offset voltage. To minimize offset, R3 should equal the parallel resistance of R1 and R2, as defined in Chapter 1. For noncritical situations, R3 can be any convenient value near the ideal value.

The Inverting Amplifier

An inverting amplifier turns the signal over 180 degrees, substituting a negative voltage for a positive one, and vice versa. It is similar to the common-emitter circuit described earlier in this chapter. An op amp will have a much lower offset voltage than the transistor circuit, and a much lower output impedance. An inverting amplifier is shown in Fig. 2-7C. The output is always equal to

$$-R2/R1$$

Gains of less than one can be had, unlike the noninverting amplifier. The input impedance is equal to R1. R3 is not critical, and can be replaced by a short in most applications. When minimum offset is required, choose R3 to equal the parallel resistance of R1 and R2.

The Summing Amplifier

The summing amplifier adds two voltages. The circuit shown in Fig. 2-7D does this, though the output is inverted. When R1, R2 and R_f are equal, there is unity gain for both inputs. Thus, if E1 = 1 V, and E2 = 1 V, then E_{Out} = −2 V. The gain for both inputs can be adjusted independently, without affecting the other. One application for this circuit is as a mixer in studio consoles. The output is defined by the formula:

$$E_{Out} = -E1(R_f/R1) - E2(R_f/R2)$$

Once again, the noninverting input grounding resistor, R3, is not critical, and can be replaced by a short. The ideal value of R3 for minimum offset is the parallel resistance of R1, R2, and R_f.

The Difference Amplifier

The difference amplifier actually subtracts the value of the inverting input from the value of the noninverting input. The circuit is shown in Fig. 2-7E. Almost always, unity gain for both inputs is required from a difference amplifier. In this case, R1 = R_f, and R2 = R3. Just make all resistors equal, and the output will be

$$E_{Out} = E2 - E1$$

The gain for the inverting input is straightforward, being

$$R1/R_f$$

The gain for the noninverting input is more complicated. If R2 were shorted, and the R1 grounded, this would be a noninverting amplifier. The gain on the noninverting input is then,

$$\frac{R1 + R_f}{R1}$$

We can then use a voltage divider to control the gain of the noninverting input. The gain of the divider will be:

$$\frac{R3}{R2 + R3}$$

Thus the gain for the noninverting input is

$$\frac{R1 + R_f}{R1} \times \frac{R3}{R2 + R3}$$

If this seems too complicated, play with the math when you're in the mood. One disadvantage of the difference amplifier is that the offset voltage can't easily be minimized by choosing an ideal value for the noninverting input grounding resistor, but this can be compensated for elsewhere in the circuit.

Types of Op Amps

The 741 is the classic op amp, a sort of silicon Model-T. Its pinouts are shown in Fig. 2-8A. When first made available in the late sixties, it cost around 30 dollars. Now

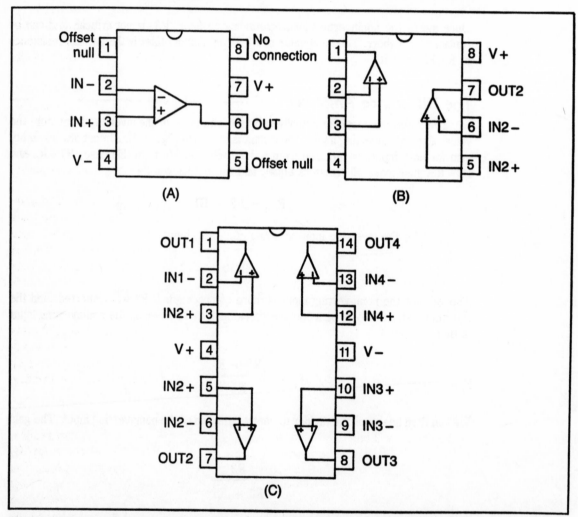

Fig. 2-8. Op amp package and pin connections. (A) 741, TL071, TL081, NE5534, LF356, LF351. (B) 1458, TL072, TL082, NE5532, LF353, 4458. (C) TL074, TL084, LF347, LM324.

24

one can be had for as little as 30 cents. While ideal for many purposes due to its low cost, it has some serious limitations. Its slew rate (the speed with which the output voltage can change value) is very low by current standards, being 0.5 V/μsec. This limits the high-frequency response. Input impedance, though respectable, is orders of magnitude lower than for devices with FET inputs, such as the TL072. The 1458 is a dual version of the 741.

The TL072 is the workhorse for the projects in this book. It costs under two dollars and has two op amps on one 8-pin chip. The pinouts are shown in Fig. 2-8B. The TL074 uses the same op amps, but mounted four to a chip (Fig. 2-8C). The TL071 is a single op amp on a chip, (Fig. 2-8A) which is not very economical, but it does provide extra terminals for nulling the output offset. Because this is not necessary for the circuits in this book, leave them unconnected if you wish to use this device. These op amps have a slew rate of 13 V/μsec, a frequency response to 3 megahertz (they can be used as detectors for AM radio signals), and an input impedance of hundreds of megohms.

The TL081, TL082, and TL084 are identical in internal circuitry to the TL07n series, but the specified noise figure is slightly higher. They are adequate for audio projects if they are more convenient to obtain. They usually cost slightly less. In fact, many TL08n devices meet TL07n specs.

Another BiFET (bipolar-FET) op amp is the LF353. Its circuitry is very different, but the specs are quite similar; it is an acceptable substitute for the TL072, being pin-for-pin compatible. The LF347 is the quad version, being a pin-for-pin replacement for the TL074. The LF351 can be used in place of the TL071.

The 4558 is another frequently encountered dual op amp. It has bipolar inputs and a very high slew rate, which makes it useful for filter circuits where a high Q is required, such as in equalizers.

The NE5534 is a low-noise op amp that is very popular among designers of professional audio gear. It does not have FET inputs, and so has the lower input impedance of a bipolar device. Its advantage is an extremely low noise figure. This is why it's used for microphone preamps in digital recorders, and in studio console boards. I question that it is worth the extra cost for most audio projects, because this op amp, and the dual version NE5532, cost about twice as much as the equivalent BiFET devices. Careful component layout and power-supply isolation will go further toward lowering noise than would substituting more expensive devices. For those who wish to use them, the NE5534 is pin compatible with the TL071, as the NE5532 is with the TL072. Power-supply requirements are about the same. For what it's worth, some golden-eared audiophiles claim that the TL072 sounds better and is more "musical" than any other op amp. They might have a point. In any case, it offers very good performance for its price.

Power-Supply Requirements

All the op amps described here require a power supply that provides both a positive and a negative voltage with respect to ground. This is called a *bipolar power supply*, not in reference to transistors, but because voltages of both polarity are present. The devices mentioned will all operate with supply rails, as they are called, of ±5 volts, though higher is better. All are rated for a maximum power supply of ±18 volts, except the 741 and the LM324, which are rated at ±15 volts. Military versions of the LF353 will tolerate ±24 volts, but these are not generally available.

One should try for the highest rate voltage, but the availability of parts might not allow this. Be assured that 12 or 15 volts will be quite acceptable for any of the projects described here. The design and construction of suitable power supplies will be described in Chapter 5.

Potential Problems

The power supply must be bypassed as close to the op amp as possible to reduce noise. This is usually done with two 0.1 μFd film capacitors, one between the positive supply and ground, and one between the negative supply and ground. Sometimes a single pair of capacitors is used for a printed circuit board, which can give acceptable results if the total distance from the caps to any op amp chip is less than a few inches. It is safer, and not very expensive, to use one pair for each op amp chip.

Both inputs of an op amp must be returned to ground, either through a resistor or through the circuitry of the preceeding stage. If this is not done, or if the resistance is too high, then the op amp will not operate. For bipolar devices, 100 kohms is the highest value that should be used. BiFET op amps will work with one or even 10 megohm impedances.

Sometimes an op amp will oscillate if the following stage or circuit becomes part of the feedback loop; this can be stopped by putting a 100-ohm resistor between the op amp's output and the succeeding stage or circuit. I have only encountered this problem once, with an LF353. Resistors cured the problem. So did using a TL072.

Perhaps the most common problem for those who design their own circuits is using leads to the inverting inputs that are too long. A review of the section on the inverting amplifier will show that without the input resistor, the gain on the minus input is equal to the open loop gain of the op amp. Because this is at least 100 dB, it means any noise picked up by the lead to this input will be magnified 100,000 times. The longer the lead, the more noise it will pick up. Keep the leads of all components that attach to an inverting input as short as possible. One audio accessory I examined had inverting input leads that ran all over the board, and were at least four inches long. It was designed by a professional, too. The noise figure, for a one-volt signal, was −66 dB in one channel, and −70 dB in the other. Proper layout could have reduced it to −90 or even −100 dB.

REFERENCES

Horowitz, Mannie. *How to Design and Build Audio Amplifiers.* Blue Ridge Summit, PA: TAB Books, Inc., 1980.

Jung, Walter G. *IC Op-Amp Cookbook.* Indianapolis, IN: Howard W. Sams & Co., Inc., 1974.

Lancaster, Don. *Active Filter Cookbook.* Indianapolis, IN: Howard W. Sams, Inc., 1975.

Lenk, John D. *Handbook for Transistors.* Englewood Cliffs, NJ: Prentice-Hall, Inc.,1976.

Staff, *The Radio Amateur's Handbook.* Newington, CT: The American Radio Relay League, 1979.

3

Construction: Tools and Techniques

Tools ARE LIKE DOLLARS—YOU CAN NEVER HAVE TOO MANY. EVEN SO, IT IS SURPRISING how few tools are really necessary to build electronic projects. The irreducible minimum would include a soldering iron, long-nosed pliers, a drill and a set of bits, and several sizes of screwdriver, both Phillips and flat blade. Add a volt-ohmmeter, and you're ready to start building. Though it's possible to build (and debug) almost any audio project with just these, more tools will make the job easier and faster. As you build more projects, you will gradually acquire a complete "wardrobe" of tools and test instruments.

TOOLS

The following is a description of tools that I have found useful in building electronics projects. It is by no means a complete catalog, but should prove useful in helping you make your own selection.

Screwdrivers

It would be nice if one screwdriver fit every screw you wanted to turn, but screws come in many sizes. If the slot of the screw is much larger than the tip of the screwdriver, you will not be able to apply enough torque to the screw to turn it tightly; you might even damage the slot in the screw head, making it impossible to turn. Once this happens, the only way to get the screw out is to drill it out. Phillips head screws require a Phillips screwdriver to turn them, though in a pinch it might be possible to use a knife blade to tighten one. This is hard on the knife blade.

For general use, two regular and two Phillips screwdrivers, large and small, are adequate. For electronics construction, a set of jeweler's screwdrivers is often convenient, and sometimes necessary. A jeweler's-size Phillips screwdriver will occasionally be required. So-called "stubby" screwdrivers, with a shank only about an inch long, make it possible to turn screws in constricted spaces.

The quality of screwdrivers can vary, and price is only a rough indicator. Look for a comfortable grip—no matter how good the quality of the blade—if you can't grasp the handle tightly, you can't use the tool properly.

Nutdrivers and Allen Wrenches

You can use pliers to grasp and turn a nut or a hex head screw, but a nutdriver does a better job. It takes perhaps one quarter the time to finish an assembly using a nutdriver instead of pliers. With a screwdriver and screw, there is some latitude for using the wrong size. With a nut driver and a nut, the fit must be exact, or it won't work. A set of half-a-dozen nutdrivers will fit most nuts you are likely to encounter.

Allen wrenches are the only tool that will turn an Allen screw. The only other way to open a cabinet held together by these fasteners is to drill out the screws.

Pliers and Wire Cutters

Standard pliers, with a set of flat, parallel jaws, and a rounded, toothed area, are not really very useful for electronics work. About all they're good for is to turn nuts. They're not even very good for that, because they tend to strip the metal from the nut's corners, turning it into a rounded nub. The next time you want to loosen the nut, the job is even harder. It's better to use a nut driver or a wrench. It is possible to hold a nut with a pair of pliers and tighten a screw into it if you hold the nut with the flat part of the jaws in such a way that the jaws are parallel to the sides of the nut. Use pliers for this purpose only if no other tool is available.

For electronics work, lineman's pliers and long-nosed pliers are much more useful, even indispensable. Lineman's pliers have blunt ends, along with cutting blades for cutting wire. They are good for dealing with heavy grades of wire, and cutting it and bending the pieces to fit under screw connectors. They are rugged enough to serve as a hammer, a use electricians routinely put them to. For electronic construction they are of limited use because something more delicate is usually needed. Long-nosed pliers fill this need. They too have diagonal wire-cutting blades and a flat surface for grasping wire, nuts, or screws. Their ends are long and pointed, making it possible to perform quite delicate manipulations. Bent-nose pliers are like long-nose, but the tip is bent at an oblique angle. They are sometimes useful for working in cramped and restricted spaces.

Diagonal pliers or cutters are wire cutters that look like a pair of pliers but have no grasping surface. There is just a pair of blades for cutting wire. They perform this task better than the blades on a pair of pliers because they offer more control.

When using the diagonal blades of pliers to strip insulation from wire, care must be taken not to nick the copper. A nick in the wire weakens it, so that it might break as you work with it. Worse, it might break after it's in the circuit, even after it has been functioning for some time. This is why wire strippers were invented.

Wire Strippers

The simplest wire strippers have two opposing blades with notches to accommodate the wires and a variable-stop mechanism to adjust for the wire's thickness. The blades descend, cut the insulation, and leave the wire unscathed. You can do the same thing with the diagonal cutters on a pair of pliers if you have a deft and sensitive hand. A sharp knife or razor blade is useful for stripping very fine wire. A knife can also be used on heavier grades of wire, so strictly speaking, wire cutters are a convenience, not a necessity. (For removing varnish insulation from magnet wire, use fine sandpaper.)

Some wire cutters are rather baroque in design, cutting the insulation and removing it from the wire, to any desired length, all with one squeeze of the hand. Such intricate mechanisms are somewhat expensive and not really necessary, unless one is stripping a great many wires.

Tweezers

Tweezers are useful for manipulating fine pieces of wire or fishing out washers that have wedged themselves behind transformers.

Drills

An electric drill is necessary to prepare a chassis for mounting parts, controls, and circuit boards. Either a quarter-inch or three-eighths-inch drill will serve for drilling metal. Variable speed is nice to have, but not a necessity. When drilling mounting holes in circuit boards, variable speed will help keep from damaging the board. (They sometimes crack or shatter.) With a fixed speed drill, clamping the board to a piece of wood before drilling will protect it. The other hazard is to the drill bit; a sixteenth-inch bit is somewhat delicate, and it is all too easy to bend and break the bit due to the weight of a standard drill. Wear goggles or safety-glasses to prevent pieces of broken bits from flying in your eyes. There are special, lightweight drills made by companies such as Dremel, but they are expensive. A hand drill can also be used. Radio Shack sells an inexpensive hand drill made especially for drilling circuit boards.

Drill Bits

Tempered bits are a necessity for working with metal. Soft bits meant for wood will quickly become dull if used to drill holes in a chassis. A set of a dozen or so assorted sizes will cover most situations. A ⅜-inch bit is necessary to make mounting holes for jack receptacles and for potentiometers. If you don't have a ⅜-inch drill, you'll have to find a ⅜-inch bit with a quarter-inch shank. A punch is sometimes included with a set of bits. It is useful for starting holes in metal; tap the punch once with a hammer or heavy pliers, and the resulting dimple in the metal will prevent the drill from walking all over the place, so you can put the hole where you want it. If you don't have a punch, a nail will do the job.

Files

A rat-tail file, or any round file, is useful for smoothing out any large holes you have to drill. Flat files are sometimes recommended for removing varnish insulation from the kind of wire used to make inductors, but I've found sandpaper is easier to use.

Soldering Irons

My grandfather built radios in the twenties. He showed me his soldering iron. It was an early cordless model. A heavy, pointed piece of steel with a wooden handle, it rested in a heavy metal rack which held it over a can of sterno. The burning sterno heated the iron to a red heat, and you were ready to solder.

Modern cordless irons use a battery and are continuously recharged when not in use. Some people swear by them because there is no cord to get in the way. Other people swear at them because they don't always give adequate heat. They are expensive.

You should probably start with a 25- or 30-watt iron, which costs about $10. A stand is also a worthwhile investment; the toy stand that comes with an inexpensive iron will not hold it securely. A larger size iron will melt your components. Larger soldering irons and soldering guns are meant for heavy-duty work, not for delicate printed circuit boards.

If you do a lot of soldering, a soldering station includes a stand with circuitry to regulate the temperature of the tip. An LED indicates when the desired temperature has been reached, and the tip will never become so hot as to be likely to damage components. Some soldering stations have digital temperature readouts. Models from the orient start at about $80 and industrial models can cost several hundred.

Tips for irons come in a variety of shapes and sizes. Chisel-shaped tips can be large or small, and conical tips are ideal for delicate work. I prefer the conical tips, and use chisel tips only when working on large, heavy boards or other components that require more heat to reach soldering temperature.

Desoldering Irons

Everybody makes mistakes, and a desoldering iron is the best way to undo an electronic error or to salvage components. This tool consists of a hollow tip and a rubber bulb. One squeezes the bulb, melts the solder with the tip, then releases the bulb, and the resulting vacuum draws the melted solder up and away, making it possible to remove components from the circuit boards. Other methods, such as braided copper wicks, do work but are not as effective. A separate bulb and nylon nozzle, meant to be used with a standard soldering iron, proved marginally effective for me.

PCB Holders

Some method of holding the board in place while components are inserted on one side, and then soldered on the other, is a great help. Various devices are available, ranging in price from $5 to $100. The more expensive units make it easier to turn the work, with more degrees of freedom, and they hold bigger boards. Even the most modest of these devices is such an improvement over trying to work on a bare workbench, it will be a welcome addition to your tool kit.

MEASURING EQUIPMENT

Some means of measuring voltage and resistance is indispensable. Decent analog

30

meters can be had for under $30. Their accuracy is typically 2%. However, these are passive devices. To measure ac voltage and current, they use a rectifying diode, and measure the resulting dc value. (The ac scale is chosen to show the true rms voltage or current.) A diode has a voltage drop of 0.7 volts; consequently, these analog meters are useless for ac voltages lower than this amount. Because it is often necessary to measure ac millivolts, an active meter is needed. In days of yore, this need was met by the VTVM, or vacuum tube volt meter. Tubes were replaced by FETs, then ICs, and now the analog movements have given way to digital counters and readouts.

Digital Multimeters

Digital multimeters, known as DMMs, and digital volt meters (DVMs) typically have 0.5% accuracy, even for the least expensive models. Prices start at about $40. Two hundred dollars can buy even better accuracy, more scales, more rugged construction, and perhaps more ergonometric design. The digital display can be read with less chance of human error than an analog scale.

One can use a DMM to sort resistors by exact value; when 1% resistors aren't available, this is a reasonable procedure.

Capacitance and Inductance Meters

There was a time when the only practical way to measure capacitance or inductance was with a Wheatstone bridge: you compared the unknown reactance to a known value, and a meter read zero when equal currents flowed in both branches of the circuit.

Digital capacitance meters will typically use an ac signal of from 8 to 800 Hz, depending on the range, measuring the effective resistance of the capacitor at this ac frequency, and calculating the capacitance from that value. Capacitance meters are very useful for sorting capacitors to obtain exact values or matches for filters and other applications that require more than the usual degree of precision. Capacitance meters can be had for under $60; most suppliers sell them for much more. Accuracy can be as high as 0.5% of a full-scale reading. More money buys more accuracy, and even the ability to measure effective series resistance (ESR), which is useful for detecting bad electrolytics. Inductance meters work in a similar fashion but are more expensive and are less often useful for most audio work.

Signal Generators

An audio signal generator can produce low-distortion sine waves at frequencies ranging from 20 Hz to 20,000 or even 200,000 Hz. For testing the frequency response of a piece of equipment or measuring the parameters of a loudspeaker, a signal generator is necessary. Accurately calibrated (5% accuracy) instruments can be purchased for as little as $150. Sometimes kits can be found for half this price. Used tube models can be had for much less, but replacement of the tubes and electrolytic capacitors would probably be necessary.

Function Generators

A function generator can produce square and triangle waves in addition to sine waves.

Some can produce voltage steps that are useful when working with digital circuits. Most function generators have more distortion than a good audio generator, but the ability to produce a square wave is a definite advantage. Viewed on an oscilloscope, the distortions of a square wave can tell an experienced technician a lot about a piece of equipment's distortion, transient response, and frequency response.

Oscilloscopes

The ability to see a wave form is a great convenience, but not always necessary. A pair of headphones can also be used to trace an audio signal through a circuit, and distortion can be heard. But if you can afford a scope, by all means get one. Used Heathkits and Eicos can be found for under $100, and even less when they aren't working. Sometimes repair means replacing the electrolytic capacitors or resoldering a cold solder joint. Other times an irreplaceable transformer might be bad, and repair will not be possible. If the cathode ray tube (CRT) is bad, replacement will cost more than a working scope. If you are willing to take a risk, a used scope might be an inexpensive alternative to a new one.

New scopes start at about $200 for a 6-MHz model. A 10-MHz triggered scope will run about $300; a dual-trace 20-MHz scope will run at least $400. Higher frequency capability costs more but is useful for TV and radio applications. For audio, any scope should have sufficient bandwidth. The feature in the costlier scopes that is most worthwhile is dual-trace capability, the simultaneous display of two signals for comparison. A scope multiplexer will convert any scope to a dual trace, but at $120 and up they aren't cheap. Still, as an upgrade for an existing instrument, this might be a good option.

Computer Accessories

If you have a computer, you can add a digital scope board with storage and analytic capabilities. For a mere thousand dollars, your IBM PC or Apple can perform the functions of a $20,000 lab scope with digital storage. You can even get an FFT (fast Fourier transform) analyzer board for about $1200. These instruments analyze the response to an impulse signal, and from it can calculate frequency and phase response, group delay, and decay time over a broad spectrum. The instrumentation microphone necessary for loudspeaker measurements will add another $1500 to the price.

The Workbench

Now that you have all these tools or plan to get them, you will need a workbench to use them properly. The more space you have, the better. The ability to spread out does make it easier to assemble projects, but even two square feet of workspace can be enough if you are neat and work carefully. A door on two sawhorses is a low-cost workbench. The main requirement is that it be stable. Whatever surface you use, it will get burned by your soldering iron sooner or later. Industrial linoleum resists scarring, but bare wood is ok if you don't mind the burn marks. Some people have covered their benches with sheet metal, but this is perhaps excessive. I, for one, find metal work surfaces unpleasant.

A shelf above the workbench for test equipment is standard practice and a very convenient way to work. I recommend you set one up as soon as you have more than one or two pieces of test equipment.

You will need drawers or a tool chest for the handtools. Another method is to use a pegboard to hold them. Everything is visible and readily at hand. If you have trouble remembering where the tools go, outline them with a magic marker. Another method used by some TV technicians is to fabricate a toolbin out of a cylinder of chicken wire. The bin is fastened to the wall above the workbench. When you're done with a tool, throw it in the bin. Most tools will also stay in place on top of the bin because they get caught in the holes in the wire mesh. Everything is out in the open and easy to find, with no effort to put things back. While I haven't tried this system, it sounds ideal for those of us who are basically lazy.

CONSTRUCTION PRACTICES

There are three ways to put together a working electronic device. A perfboard is a sheet of phenolic material with a gridwork of holes. Components are mounted and held in place by their wire leads, which are threaded through the holes. Connections are made by point-to-point wiring soldered in place. This method is adequate for the simplest, least demanding circuits, such as power supplies. For anything more complicated or less robust, it won't do.

Wire wrap is a system in which special mounting posts are affixed to a perfboard; components are soldered to these posts, and thin wire is wrapped about the posts; the sharp corner edges on the posts pierce the wire's insulation, making a solderless connection. This method is used for making working prototypes for non-audio applications. For digital circuits, rf interference can be horrendous with this method, interfering with the device's function. For audio, there is a risk of noise, and this method is seldom used. Printed circuits are the preferred construction technique.

Printed Circuit Boards

Printed circuit boards can be custom fabricated, or pre-etched general purpose breadboards can be purchased from a number of suppliers. Radio Shack carries several different styles. The base material is often a phenolic plastic; better quality boards use a glass-epoxy compound. The conductor is invariably copper, though gold plating is sometimes used for connector contacts. If you must solder to gold, try to remove it with very fine sandpaper; the gold will dissolve in the solder, perhaps interfering with the bond. Tin plated boards are fine for soldering.

The procedure for designing a board starts by determining a parts layout; this is done by drawing the components on graph paper, and then drawing in the connecting leads. Parts are often moved around during this process. Then the design is transferred to transparent plastic acetate. Decals are available with round pads for standard components, such as DIP ICs and transistors. Sometimes the design can be drawn directly on a copper-plated board, using etch-resistant decals and india ink, but photo transfer from acetate artwork gives better results, and allows multiple copies. To prepare a board for etching, it is coated with a photosensitizer, then exposed to light passed through the acetate artwork. The exposed PC board is put in a developer, which makes the exposed pattern visible, and an etching bath, which removes the copper that is not protected by the photo-pattern of the etch resist. The etch resist is removed with another chemical, (household ammonia does a fair job) and the board is ready for drilling. Both positive and negative transfer systems are in use. Pre-sensitized PC boards are sold. Companies will make finished boards from artwork for a steep fee. For a simple audio circuit, this procedure is overkill.

Printed circuit breadboards are pre-etched and predrilled. The patterns accommodate rows of ICs, and these patterns are readily adapted to circuits of moderate complexity. All of the circuits in this book are simple enough to be built this way.

The process of mounting parts on a PC board is called "stuffing." Stuff a board by mounting the components in this order: IC sockets followed by resistors, then capacitors, the small ones first, then the larger ones, finishing with the electrolytics. In general, the small, low-lying parts are mounted first, followed by the larger components. If you are doing a parts layout on a pre-etched board, start with the ICs, spaced far enough apart that you will not be cramped for space. Hook up the leads for the power supply for each chip, and then insert the decoupling capacitors. Follow the principles of parts layout given in Chapter 2 in the section on op amps. Working one stage at a time, place the resistors and capacitors, working from the schematic. Add any necessary jumper wires. Use solid #22 or #24 gauge insulated wire. Remember, leads to the negative input of an op amp must be as short as possible. Proceed one stage at a time. Double-check your work as you go, and again when you are done before applying power. It is best to solder as you go, two or three parts at a time, or components will fall in your lap. Some people prefer to draw the layout of all components before building, others find it easier to do the layout with the actual components, as described. With practice, this procedure becomes easier. Start with simple circuits, and work up to the ones using several op amps.

If the task of doing your own layout is too daunting, Rivera audio has worked out stuffing guides for the projects in this book, to be used with readily available pre-etched PC boards, which are available for a modest fee. See the Appendix for more information.

Soldering

Poor soldering is the cause of most project failures. (Reversed power-supply leads account for most of the rest.) Even if the soldering is done properly, no book or instruction manual I've seen tells you that you have to degrease the board before attempting to solder it. Radio Shack does include an instruction sheet with some of its PC boards suggesting that you use sandpaper or steel wool on the board before soldering. It isn't enough. Degreasing is necessary. Chemical compounds are made expressly for degreasing PC boards. Trichloroethane is an active ingredient in many of these products, and is also found in commercial spot removers sold in supermarkets and hardware stores. Carbonna is one brand I've found that effectively prepares a board for soldering without damaging it. Pure isopropyl alcohol, sometimes found in tape-head cleaners, also works. Avoid rubbing alcohol as sold in drug stores. It is too dilute, and contains perfumes and oils that might interfere with a good bond.

Many instruction manuals and textbooks say to solder a component by putting the wire between the iron tip and the solder, and waiting until the wire is heated sufficiently for the solder to melt and flow between the wire and the board or lug. This was fine for building tube equipment, but transistors and low-voltage components are likely to be damaged if you use this technique. Instead, hold the iron so that the tip touches both the wire and the board. After one or two seconds, touch the solder simultaneously to both the wire and the board (or any other component, lug, or thing you are soldering. See Fig. 3-1.) If the joint has been heated enough, the solder will flow between the parts. Remove the solder, then the iron, as soon as this occurs. The iron should contact the board and component no more than four seconds. Otherwise, the component might be damaged or the copper foil might separate from the board. If four seconds isn't enough, you might need a bigger tip or a higher wattage iron. Avoid moving the parts while the solder cools, or you will have a "cold solder joint," which will cause problems due to its poor conductivity. You can tell when the solder solidifies; it changes color slightly. It should remain shiny. A gray, crystaline appearance indicates a bad joint; you will have to reheat and try again, perhaps removing excess solder. The solder should wet over the entire area of the board it contacts. If it beads up, resistance of the joint might be too high, so try again. One thing helps make a good joint: it should be mechanically sound before solder is applied. If soldering to a lug, bend and crimp the wire about the metal so that it holds firmly even without solder. When pushing leads through circuit boards, bend them on the foil side, so they won't pop out when you let go to pick up the solder. Pre-tinning an unclad copper board with solder can make the soldering of components easier and faster, but be careful not to clog the holes in the board.

The tip of the iron must be kept clean and shiny. A damp sponge is used for this purpose. Most soldering stands will have a small tray with a sponge for cleaning the tip. A small amount of nondetergent household ammonia diluted with water is more effective than water alone. After soldering each joint, wipe the tip on the sponge, cleaning off bits of oxidized rosin. If the tip gets really dirty, you can clean it off with fine sandpaper (when it's cool) then re-tin it with some solder, so it is smooth and shiny. If you sand too much, you will remove the iron coating and expose the copper center of the

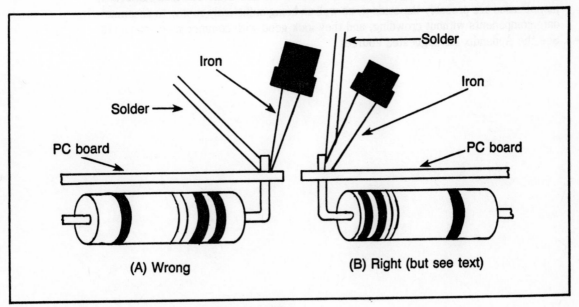

Fig. 3-1. Soldering a component. (A) Wrong. (B) Right.

tip. It will then have to be replaced because the copper will dissolve in the solder, making it bond poorly.

A trick that helps when soldering heat-sensitive components, such as ICs, precision resistors, and low-voltage plastic capacitors, is to place the component side of the board on top of a damp sponge before soldering. The sponge acts as a heat sink, sucking up heat that would otherwise damage parts. I only take this precaution when soldering ICs directly to a board, or when using 1% components in a circuit where a slight change in value due to heat would be undesirable. Plastic film capacitors rated at under 100 volts are particularly vulnerable to heat damage, and this technique helps protect them. Unless you have a heavy hand with the soldering iron, this trick will not otherwise be necessary.

The type of solder used is important. Rosin core solder is a must. Acid core solder, used for plumbing and sheet metal work, will corrode your board and components. Rosin is an organic compound that wets the metal, so the solder flows freely and coats it evenly. For PC boards, the thinner and finer the solder, the easier it will be to use; 0.032 gauge is ideal and 0.050 will do, but it is harder to work with.

After you have finished soldering, you will have to clean the rosin residue off the board. If you don't, its corrosive properties can damage your project in a matter of months. Flux removers are made specifically for this purpose. Pure isopropyl alcohol will remove flux, but can damage components. Polystyrene capacitors are especially vulnerable. If care is exercised, such compounds can be used. Some commercial flux removers are claimed not to damage parts, but it is still best to be cautious.

Cases

Once you have assembled the board, you'll have to put it in a box. Cases are often the most expensive part of a project, and the hardest to find. Nineteen-inch black rackmount cases are probably the sexiest, as well as being sufficiently roomy to accommodate components without crowding, and they look good with commercial components. See the Appendix for suggested sources.

4
Projects Without Power Supplies

P ASSIVE CIRCUITS HAVE NO POWER SUPPLIES. THE TERM "PASSIVE CIRCUITS" SOUNDS wimpy, but these are really powerful, sophisticated projects that can add much to your system. For the beginner, these projects have the advantage of being relatively simple, and give you experience of soldering and installing components in chassis.

SURROUND SOUND

Most movies today are made using the Dolby Labs' surround sound process. Besides the right and left stereo channels, there are extra "surround sound" channels, used for special effects and added spatial ambience. There are actually three versions of this process, which can have as many as six discreet channels. The 70-millimeter prints of a film will use four or six channels, and will have magnetic sound tracks. The 35-mm prints have two optical sound tracks, which contain a matrixed version of the surround sound channels. It is the 35-mm soundtrack which finds its way onto videotape and into your home. If you already feed the output from your hi-fi VCR through your stereo, it is a relatively simple matter to add surround sound to your system. Units to dematrix soundtracks cost several hundred dollars, and sometimes need an extra amplifier as well. A passive dematrixer, while not quite up to the standards of a digital surround sound processor, is still a good performer, with a much better cost/performance ratio.

Bringing It All Back Home

The circuits to de-matrix surround sound develop an R-L and an L-R difference sig-

37

nal. This signal has been treated with Dolby© noise reduction, and a modified Dolby circuit cuts the highs in the proper proportion. A 15- to 30- millisecond time delay is applied to these signals, and the highs are rolled off above 7000 Hz. The time delay ensures that patrons sitting near the theater's surround speakers won't hear them before the signal from the main speakers arrives. There are further bells and whistles: a subwoofer to reproduce the gut-wrenching impact of earthquakes, explosions, and car crashes, and a center channel to keep dialogue centered on the screen.

The center channel is not so important for home use, unless your speakers are excessively far apart. One can always add a subwoofer to a system, perhaps using one of the active crossovers in Chapter 9, or the bass-enhancing filter of Chapter 8. The difference signals can be generated using the op amp difference amplifier described in Chapter 2, but there is a simpler way. The Dynaco quadraphonic matrix, popular in the early seventies during the height of quadraphonic sound, will produce the difference signals without using electronics and an extra amplifier. This circuit is diagrammed in Fig. 4-1.

The 15-millisecond time delay is not as important at home as in a theater, where you have less control over the seating accommodations. One millisecond is roughly the time it takes sound to travel one foot. If the surround speakers are placed fifteen feet further behind you than the main speakers are in front of you, this will achieve a fifteen millisecond delay. It also requires a huge room at least 35 feet long. Fortunately, compromising the time delay is not so disastrous in the home environment as in a theater. Shorter distances will give acceptable results, as long as the main speakers are a couple of feet closer to the listener than the surround speakers. Another expedient is to put the surround speakers down the hall or in an adjoining room. This has given acceptable results, adding a great deal of spaciousness to many a film's soundtrack. Another possibility which I have not yet tried is to point the surround speakers away from the listening area so that the sound bounces off the rear and side walls before being heard, adding delay due to its path length.

Rolling off the high frequencies above 7000 Hz in the surround speakers is the last remaining step. It could be done by putting an inductor in series with the surround speakers. I prefer to diminish the tweeters' response by mechanical means. Remove the grill cover from the speakers you intend to use for the rear channel, and put a piece of tightly woven fabric, such as from a pillowcase, over each tweeter. Hold the fabric in place by any convenient means, such as tape, thumbtacks, or staples. A layer of plastic kitchen wrap also blocks high frequencies while passing the midrange, and may be used in conjunction with fabric, so fewer layers are required. The idea is to get most of the midrange sound while muffling the highs. This method also makes up for the fact that the surround signal is Dolbyized, so no decoder is needed. You might wish to experiment with various amounts of covering over the tweeter; just how much is needed is a function both of the particular driver you are treating, and the fabric covering you are using. I suggest starting with one layer of fabric and one layer of plastic wrap. If this gives satisfactory results, go no further.

The choice of speakers for the surround channel is not terribly critical. They need not match your present speakers, which could be an expensive proposition. The surround speakers are not called on to produce much base, and so can be quite small. There are several inexpensive models sold by Radio Shack that will do quite nicely. Some have four-inch woofer/midranges with one-inch tweeters. Others, less expensive, have a sin-

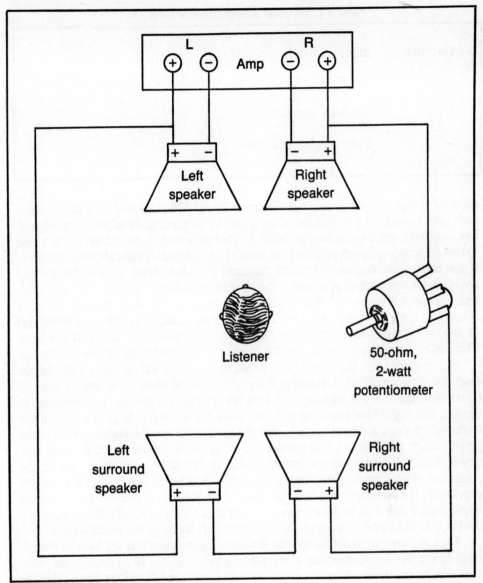

Fig. 4-1. Surround sound decoder circuit.

gle, three- or four-inch driver. These probably roll off above 7000 Hz, and so no treatment will be necessary. If such single-driver speakers produce surround effects that are too brilliant or zingy, due to too good a high-frequency response, try angling them away from the main listening area; the highs on such a driver should be very directional, and turning the speakers can bring out the off-axis response, which will have fewer highs.

Construction

The parts list for this project is shown in Table 4-1. The potentiometer should be

Table 4-1. Surround Sound Decoder Parts List.

Quantity	Item
1	2-watt potentiometer; any value between 20 and 100 ohms
1 pair	Auxiliary speakers,
—	case, speaker terminals

rated for at least two watts. Any value between 25 and 100 ohms is okay. Unfortunately, such pots are not easy to find these days, and some scrounging might be necessary. See suggested suppliers in the Appendix. It is not necessary to mount the pot in a case to test the system, though soldering the leads to its terminals is strongly recommended. If you like the results, the pot can be mounted in a case. Many pots of this wattage are made for screwdriver adjustment, rather than using a knob mounted to a shaft. Because the pot will seldom be adjusted after the initial setup, this is no handicap. Terminal connectors are a nicety and make the unit fully transportable. You can use a second set of speaker terminals on your receiver for sending the signal to the surround speakers. This makes it possible to switch the unit in and out without having to wire in a switch.

A cautionary note: the extra load imposed by the additional speakers might be too much for some amplifiers. Generally, there will be no problem if the amp is rated at 60 watts or more. If the manufacturer does not recommend driving extra speakers in parallel, you might have problems with less powerful amplifiers. In such a case, if the additional speakers are more efficient than the main speakers, the proper setting of the potentiometer will ensure a high enough load so as not to bother the amp. Most low-power amps will deliver enough current so that there will be no problem, but for the protection of your amps, a two-amp speaker fuse at the amp output, which is usually provided by the manufacturer, should be used. This will keep the output transistors from burning out if called on to deliver more current than they can handle. If you have any doubts that this circuit is suitable for your amplifier, write to the manufacturer.

Once the decoder is set up and the speakers are in place, you will have to experiment to find the optimum setting of the potentiometer. Listen to an appropriate video tape, one where the movie was made in Dolby© stereo, and turn down the level of the surround speakers until you are not normally aware of their presence, but only hear something from behind at an appropriate moment in the film. Ordinary stereo source material, such as a record or CD, can also be used to make the adjustment. Turn down the setting of the pot until the surround speakers just seem to disappear as a source of sound. You will find that though you don't hear them, the sound field seems to collapse toward the front of the room when they are suddenly disconnected.

A PASSIVE IMAGE ENHANCER

One of the more interesting stereo add-on devices is the image enhancer. This device cancels the interaural cross-talk caused by the fact that each ear hears both speakers.

By electronically canceling the extra signal, one can expand the sound stage and produce three dimensional sonic effects. At its best, the result is like those binaural recordings made with microphones placed in the ears of a dummy head, and played back through headphones. The realism of such recordings is astonishing. The results of image enhancement can be equally astonishing in their realism. The circuitry required for this project is the same as for the surround sound decoder.

The first such devices were electronic, such as Carver's "Sonic Holography," and Sound Concepts' "Image Restoration System." Passive devices, relying on extra speakers, are also possible, and such speaker systems have been produced.

It is relatively simple to set up a passive image enhancement system if you already have a stereo system; the only additional components required are a potentiometer and an extra pair of speakers. This effect is well worth experimenting with; at its best, it can give an uncanny solidity to reproduced music, by moving the apparent sound source out from between the speakers and into the room. There is a certain thrill to hearing cymbals at your elbow, while a female vocalist nibbles on your ear.

How Image Enhancement Works

The principle on which image enhancement is based is that both speakers are heard by each ear, which makes the degradation of stereo separation and imaging inevitable. Listen to your system. Even with your eyes closed, it is always possible to tell where the speakers are, nor can your system produce a sound that is further left than the left speaker, nor further right than the right.

The reason for this is illustrated in Fig. 4-2A. The signal from the left speaker is also heard by the right ear, delayed and attenuated by a factor of alpha due to the longer path length involved. Electronic image enhancers produce the same delay and attenuation in the left-channel signal and then invert it, and mix it with the right channel. It arrives at the right ear and cancels out the undesired signal (and vice versa for the other channel.) Passive circuits can do this if the delayed and attenuated signal is reproduced by a separate speaker, as shown in Fig 4-2B. (Those of you who have followed this explanation might be wondering what happens to the inverted cancellation signal when it arrives at the opposite ear. Because it is doubly attenuated and delayed, it is no longer significant in determining localization.)

The actual implementation is not quite so simple. The high frequencies must be attenuated above 6000 Hz, because these frequencies are not diffracted around the listener's head. If they were to appear in the cancellation signal, they would make the overall sound too brilliant.

When this process is successfully carried out, each ear only hears the signal from one channel, much as is the case with headphones, but the sound stage doesn't appear to be inside one's head. Instruments can be to the far right or far left, or they might even be at your elbow. There are some disadvantages: the ideal listening position is more circumscribed than normal, and the effect is not suited to every recording.

Ideally, you will want four identical speakers to set up your own image enhancer, but this is not strictly necessary. Precise localization can suffer unless the speakers are very well matched in terms of frequency response, but the general ambience will come across even if the positioning is less than precise. I recommend that you experiment with inexpensive speakers before duplicating your main speakers. The imaging speakers

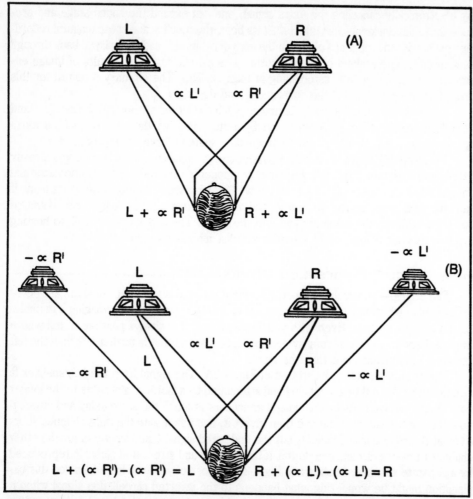

Fig. 4-2. With normal stereo (A), each ear picks up a delayed, attenuated version of the signal meant for the other ear. This degrades separation and imaging. By feeding to each ear signals that cancel the interaural crosstalk (B), imaging and separation are restored. (Courtesy Audio magazine.)

should roll off sharply above six or seven thousand Hz, so use the same attenuation procedure described for the surround sound decoder.

The electrical hookup is shown in Fig. 4-3. It is electrically identical to the surround sound decoder and the old Dynaco Quad decoder. Like these systems, it uses only the difference, or L - R, signal. This part of the signal carries all of the directional information, so it is sufficient to use it alone. There is also an added advantage in that bass is primarily nondirectional and mono. It will not be reproduced this way, so your amp will not be overloaded as easily as it would be if you were simply driving an extra pair of speakers in parallel to the main ones. This is why you will hear very little bass when you listen to just the imaging speakers. If the sound source has very little directional information, you won't hear anything at all.

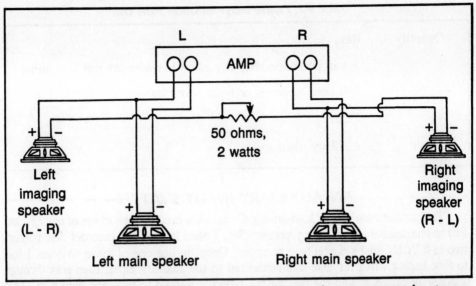

Fig. 4-3. Wiring diagram of a passive image-recovery system using two extra speakers to produce an inverted, crossfed difference signal. Attenuation is controlled by the rheostat-wired potentiometer shown, and time delay is controlled by the position of the speakers. (Courtesy Audio magazine.)

Construction

The parts list for this project is shown in Table 4-2.

Construction is the same as for the surround sound decoder, and the same precautions apply regarding your power amplifier. The same box and speakers can be used for both circuits; only the speaker locations are different. (I have not tried using both setups simultaneously and can't comment on the sonic results, but the load on your amplifier may be excessive.) When the system is set up, what you will hear from the imaging speakers will be quieter than the sound from the left and right speakers, with very little bass present. Nonetheless, this signal greatly expands the stereo sound stage.

Positioning Imaging Speakers

To position the imaging speakers, you will want to keep their path length to the listener about six inches longer than that of the main speakers. Most "bookshelf" speakers, with drivers no larger than eight inches, can be placed next to each other to achieve this. Larger systems will require you to move the imaging speakers forward slightly. It is also possible to stack the speakers, putting the imaging speakers on top of the main ones. Also, the ideal listening position will be different than for normal stereo: the effect works best when the speakers are slightly closer together than is usually the case. The optimum distance to the listener should be approximately the ratio shown in Fig. 4-4. You will want to adjust the pot so that the signal from the imaging speakers is 3 to 6 dB down with respect to that from the main speakers, or about half as loud. If you follow these rough guidelines, a minimum of experimentation will be necessary to get the best results.

Table 4-2. Passive Image Enhancer Parts List.

Quantity	Item
1	2-watt potentiometer; any value between 20 and 100 ohms
3	Pair binding posts, or push terminals
1	Case
1 pair	Auxiliary speakers

AN AUXILIARY INPUT SWITCH

The proliferation of new high-fidelity devices has created a shortage of input jacks. I have one auxiliary input on my preamplifier. I need to plug in a compact disc player, two hi-fi VCRs, and a digital tape recorder. Once, to use one of these devices, I had to first unplug whatever else was connected to the auxiliary input, then sort through a tangle of cables to find the one for the device I wanted to use, and plug it in. This inconvenience was mild compared to getting at the back of the preamplifier. It would have been possible to use the tape monitor inputs, but there were two cassette decks plugged into those.

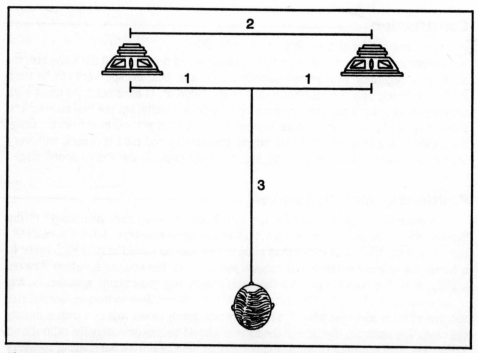

Fig. 4-4. For optimum image recovery, the listener should be positioned on the centerline between the speakers, 1-½ times as far from the speakers as they are from each other. (Courtesy Audio magazine.)

44

A perfectly good preamp without enough inputs must be a widespread problem, because so many new hi-fidelity products are becoming available. The solution is obvious, too. If you don't want to trade in your preamp or receiver, you need an outboard switch box. This sounds simple, but try to find one. I couldn't. Why some enterprising manufacturer hasn't marketed one is inexplicable, but the only solution to the input shortage seems to be to build your own switch box. This project is a Radio-Shack special. They sell a six-position two-pole rotary switch, which should provide a more than adequate number of inputs (see Catalog #275-1386). A sufficiently roomy box (such as their #270-253), some phono jacks (#274-346), a knob, and some 22 gauge wire are all the parts needed. By using a metal box that provides adequate shielding, it is possible to use single-strand wire instead of shielded cable.

Construction

The parts list for this switch is shown in Table 4-3.

Drilling holes in the box must be done with care, as it will affect the finished look of the project. Use a ruler and felt-tip pen to lay out the locations of the jacks and the switch, (the water-soluble ink will wash off with a damp sponge) and use a metal punch (or a hammer and nail) to "dimple" the site of the intended hole. This makes it possible to drill accurately. Start with small holes, ⅛ inch, and work up to ¼ inch for the jacks. You will need a ⅜-inch bit for the switch. Remove metal burrs from the holes with a rat-tail file. You will need a second hole, approximately ⅛ inch, for the stop-tab that prevents the switch from rotating. Mount the switch and the phono jacks.

You are now ready to wire the unit. The two input jacks go to the two inner solder tabs on the switch. Examination of the switch structure will show which pairs of tabs to use for an output and in what order to connect them. Even if the rotating wipers weren't visible, a continuity tester or an ohmmeter would make it possible to determine this information. Note: the ground lugs of all the phono jacks for each individual channel should be wired together to assure a good ground connection. The two channels' grounds needn't be cross-connected. Only the inner or "hot" lead from the jacks needs to be connected to the switch. This is illustrated in Fig. 4-5. Only one channel is shown in the illustration, for clarity. The jacks for the second channel are mounted immediately below those shown for the first channel. Only one output is shown wired to further simplify things. Twisted-pair wiring is shown. Place two equal lengths of wire side by side, and twist them together to make a length of twisted-pair wire. There should be four to six turns per inch. If the box is well shielded, you can probably get away with single wires, but there would be a possibility of crosstalk, or signal leakage, unless great care is taken laying out the wires, avoiding parallel runs. By twisting a ground wire about the signal wire, crosstalk and noise can be greatly reduced or eliminated. The ground wires are

Table 4-3. Auxiliary Input Switch Parts List.

Quantity	Item
1	2-gang, 6-pole switch
1	Case, phono jacks as needed

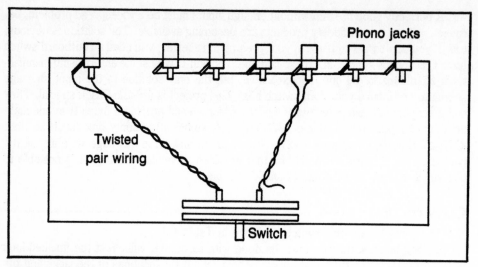

Fig. 4-5. Auxiliary switch box.

left floating at the switch. If they were connected here as well as at the jacks, there would be a danger of forming a ground loop, introducing hum into the circuitry. The ground lugs of the phono jacks are all interconnected, to provide a common round signal path.

You will probably want to shorten the switch's shaft with a hacksaw. A professional look can be obtained by labeling the switch positions, inputs, and outputs with dry transfers (Radio Shack #270-201), but I found it more convenient to use a fine-point permanent felt-tip pen and write the labels by hand. There are sealed switches made with gold and silver contacts. These will last longer than the Radio Shack switch without growing noisy as they age, but they are more expensive and harder to locate. See the Appendix for a mail-order source.

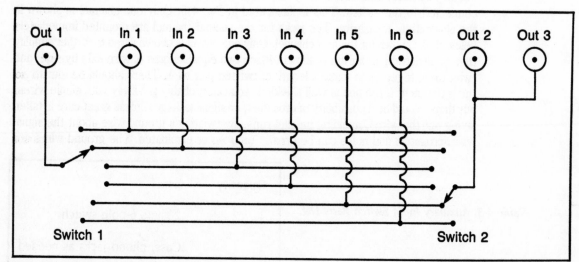

Fig. 4-6. A dual-output switch box.

Further Refinements

You can make tape monitoring and dubbing possible by adding a second switch. This is shown schematically for one channel in Fig. 4-6. If output-one is feeding your preamplifier from a CD player, you can be feeding a VCR from output two, and record the hi-fi soundtrack from a second VCR while you listen to the CD. A third output is shown in parallel to output two, which can be used for another recording device. If your receiver doesn't have dual tape-monitoring loops and dubbing capabilities, you might well want to add this second switch.

The addition of a dual gang potentiometer for use as a volume control will turn the switchbox into a rudimentary preamplifier, one without any active circuitry. I will discuss this further in Chapter 6.

5

Power Supplies

Y OU WILL NEED A POWER SUPPLY FOR MOST ELECTRONIC PROJECTS. THIS CHAPTER covers the principles of operation, the components, and shows how to build several practical supplies for different applications.

────────────TRANSFORMERS AND RECTIFIERS────────────

A transformer serves two functions. It steps down the 120-volt line voltage to a value compatible with the electronic devices being used, and it isolates the device from the full line current. Without this isolation, a short could place the chassis at full line potential, which could create a lethal shock and fire hazard. After the electrical voltage has been transformed to a suitable value, it must be rectified, or converted from ac to dc. Figure 5-1 shows several rectifier circuits and the resulting dc waveforms they produce. The half wave rectifier in Fig. 5-1A is not very efficient, as can be seen from the wave form it produces: half the time its output is zero, so it can't supply much current on a steady basis. Instead, the full-wave bridge (Fig. 5-1B) and half-wave center tap (Fig. 5-1C) circuits are used where a single polarity voltage is needed. Most op amp and amplifier circuits work best with split supplies, as shown in Fig. 5-1D. While this circuit looks like a full-wave bridge, it is really two half-wave center-tapped circuits of opposite polarity. The result is a power supply with both positive and negative, as well as ground, potentials.

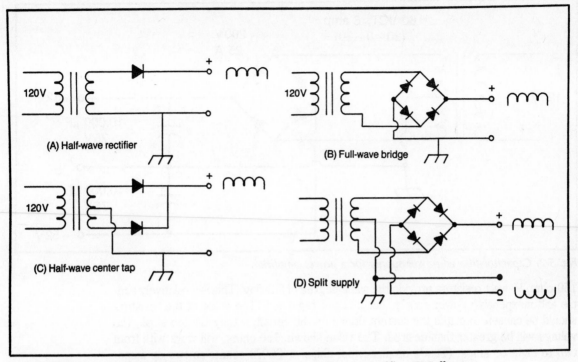

Fig. 5-1. *Rectifier circuits and their resulting waveforms. (A) Half-wave rectifier. (B) Full-wave bridge. (C) Half-wave center-tapped. (D) Split supply.*

Power-Supply Filtering

So far, these circuits transform ac into pulsating dc. The dc must be filtered to remove the ripple. The simplest way to do this is with a large capacitor. Figure 5-2 shows such a power supply, one that is suitable for a 100-watt power amplifier such as the one to be described in Chapter 6. The transformer is 60-volts center-tapped, rated at 5 amps. The capacitors' voltage rating should be greater than the peak voltage from the transformer, or at least 1.4 times the rms output voltage of the transformer. Because the capacitors store electrons, the power supply is able to deliver a steady dc voltage equal to the peak ac voltage. This is only true for a light load. Under full load, such as when an amplifier is called on to deliver sustained high-power signals, the available voltage drops toward the rms value. The capacitors for such a supply must be quite large, and hence expensive. Because they are so large and heavy, it is not practical to mount such capacitors on a circuit board with other components. Instead, special mounting hardware is used to mount the caps to the chassis, and heavy gauge wire is used to connect the capacitors to the rest of the circuit.

One way of reducing the capacitor requirements for an op amp power supply is shown in Fig. 5-3. It is not used for power amplifiers because the resistors would consume too much power, making it too inefficient to be practical, but it is well suited for powering several op amps. Instead of two 10,000-μF capacitors, four 1000-μF caps, and two

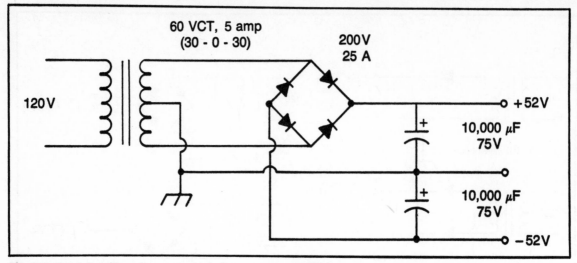

Fig. 5-2. Capacitor-filtered power supply for a power amplifier.

150-ohm, ½-watt resistors provide the same degree of filtering. This is a relatively simple and inexpensive power supply, but it is not regulated. The value of the resistors should be chosen to match the current drawn by the circuit; if they are too small, the voltage will be greater than desired. The value shown, 150 ohms, will work with from two to eight op amps. (That's op amps, not chips: a TL072 counts as two op amps, not one.) If the output voltage is measured with no load, it will be higher than it would be with some op amps connected. The voltage will also vary with the op amps' demand for power, as under peak signal conditions. Another problem is that 24-volt transformers aren't as readily available as 25.4-volt ones. To use the 25.4-volt transformer with this

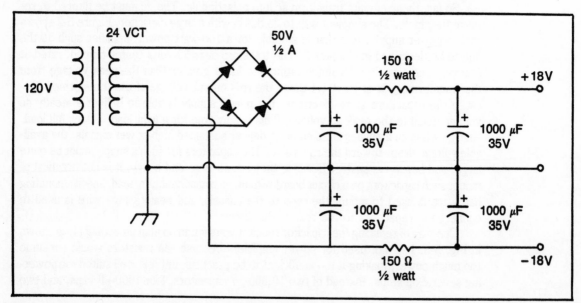

Fig. 5-3. Capacitor-resistor filtered power supply for op amps.

supply would mean using a larger resistor, which would waste power and generate heat. Some means of regulation would eliminate these problems.

─────────────────────────REGULATION─────────────────────────

Regulation improves the rejection of power-supply ripple, which is heard as hum, and allows the supply to deliver the same voltage over a much greater range of current demand. The simplest way to obtain regulation is with a zener diode, as shown in Fig. 5-4. The input voltage must be at least five volts higher than the zener voltage, or the diode won't regulate. The capacitor must be fairly large, at least 1000 μF, and the value of the resistor is dependent on the current to be drawn by the load and on the power rating of the zener diode. The resistor must be large enough to ensure that the zener diode will not be called on to dissipate too much power. This limits the maximum power available to the load and wastes power. Figure 5-5 shows one way to extend a zener's power-handling capability and not waste power heating a current-limiting resistor. The transistor is connected as an emitter follower, and will pass roughly ten times as much current as the zener diode; due to the voltage drop across the base-emitter junction, the regulated voltage is 0.7 volts greater than the zener voltage. This power supply is not bullet proof; if called on to deliver too much power, as might happen if the output were shorted, either or both of the semiconductors could burn out. Another transistor could be used to provide current limiting and assure that the power supply would survive such abuse. More parts would provide over-voltage and short-circuit shutdown, but the number of parts required becomes prohibitive, as does the time required to calculate the component values. Those readers interested in designing their own discrete power supplies can explore the reference given at the end of the chapter, but there is a much faster, easier, and inexpensive way to build a regulated power supply.

The IC Regulator───

Integrated circuit regulators look like transistors, but they contain a dozen or more transistors and associated components. One regulator and two capacitors will provide a stable, highly regulated power source, with both current limiting and overload protection. Figure 5-6 shows the pin configurations for typical positive and negative voltage regulators, and a circuit diagram illustrating their use. This circuit is the basic power

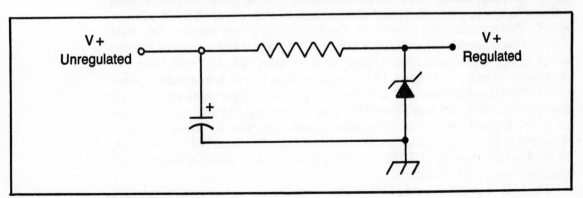

Fig. 5-4. A zener diode regulator.

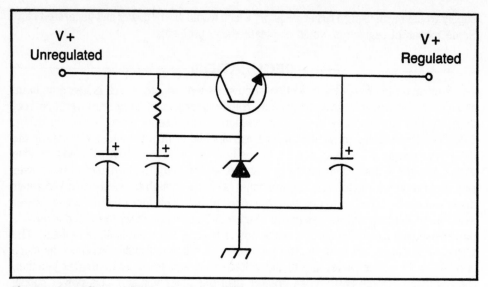

Fig. 5-5. Extending a zener's current capability with an emitter follower.

supply for most of the projects in this book. The 7815 is a positive 15-volt regulator in a TO-220 case, and the 7915 is a negative 15-volt regulator. Note that the pin configurations of the positive and negative regulators are not the same; I was once burned by this, or more precisely, I burned up a negative regulator by trying to connect it as if it were positive. The 7915 smoked and died. I was lucky to have a second one on hand. For the positive regulator, pin 1 is the unregulated dc input, pin 3 is the regulated output, and pin 2 is the ground reference. For the negative regulator, the input and ground pins are reversed. This holds true for all 78nn and 79nn regulators.

The last two digits signify the output voltage for this type of regulator. The 78 prefix indicates a positive regulator, and the 79 prefix indicates a negative regulator. Thus, 7812 is a positive 12-volt regulator, and 7915 is a negative 15-volt regulator. These devices will supply up to an amp of current and are available in sizes ranging from 5 to 24 volts. The 15-volt regulators are probably best for these projects, and the 12-volt ones will suffice. Generally, the higher the voltage the better, up to the maximum voltage rating of the devices being powered. Though most modern op amps are rated for 18-volt supply rails, they sometimes fail prematurely if operated from 18-volt supplies. This might be due to the regulators delivering slightly too much voltage. I have measured voltages as high as 18.2 volts from a 7818. Though this is unusually high, 18.1 volts is not that uncommon. Whatever the reason, 15-volt supplies seem to give more reliable results.

Three-amp regulators in a TO-220 case are made. Low-power regulators are available in TO-92 cases, and high-power TO-3 case devices that can deliver more power are made. There are also adjustable regulators, which can vary the voltage delivered to the load by varying the voltage on the ground terminal. For the projects in this book, the fixed voltage, one-amp, TO-220 devices are recommended. Anything else will likely cost more and provide no advantage.

The LM340 (positive) and LM320 (negative) regulators are functionally equivalent to the 78nn and 79nn devices. Their voltages are indicated by a numeric suffix in the catalogs, such as LM340-15; this denotes a 15-volt positive regulator. Unfortunately, the suffix does not always get printed on the case, which makes it difficult to identify what you've got in your parts bin without testing the output in a circuit. This is why I prefer the 78nn devices, because even in the neatest shop, some parts get in the wrong bin. There might be another reason to prefer the 78's and 79's. One British hi-fi magazine claims they give superior regulation by a factor of ten, and thus make it possible to build quieter equipment. Perhaps, though I have seen no actual measurements supporting this claim.

These regulators can be mounted on a heat sink in order to take full advantage of

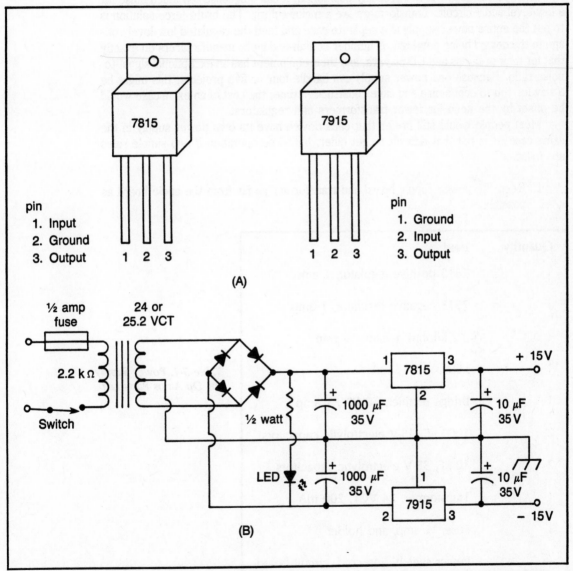

Fig. 5-6. Voltage regulators. (A) Three-terminal fixed-voltage regulators. (B) Regulated 15-volt power supply.

their power-handling capability, but for op amp projects this is not really necessary. Mount the regulators so the leads hold the case about a quarter inch above the circuit board; this allows the leads to dissipate heat, instead of allowing heat to build up at the bottom of the case. The regulator will still get quite warm, but this is all right as long as air can circulate freely around it. The project cabinet may be sealed if it is large, but a small cabinet will probably need ventilation holes.

POWER-SUPPLY CONSTRUCTION

The parts list for this project is shown in Table 5-1.

If the power supply is not properly positioned, it can still cause too much noise for a low-level audio circuit. Transformers are a major culprit. The brute-force solution is to put the entire power supply in a separate case and feed the regulated low-level voltage to the device being powered. A number of high-end audio manufacturers do exactly that for their preamps and CD players, and their equipment has an exceptional signal-to-noise ratio. Because one power supply can handle four or five projects, this might be a way for you to economize and save construction time; the cost of an extra case would be offset by the need for fewer transformers and regulators.

Most people would still prefer that each device have its own power supply in the same case. It is not that difficult to get quiet, hum-free operation if two simple rules are followed:

1. Keep the power supply board and transformer as far from the audio board as possible.

Quantity	Item
1	7815 positive regulator, 1 amp
1	7915 negative regulator, 1 amp
1	2.2 kilohm resistor, ½ watt
1	LED
1	Bridge rectifier, 50 PIV, 1 amp
2	1000 μF, 35-V electrolytic capacitors
2	10 μF, 35-V electrolytic capacitors
1	Transformer, 24 VCT, 200 mA
1	Fuse, ½ amp, and holder
—	Power switch, line cord, circuit board

Table 5-1. Power Supply for Op Amps Parts List.

2. Keep the signal leads away from power leads, and away from the transformer.

The basic layout for any audio project has the transformer well away from the sensitive audio circuits. The signal leads go on the right side of the case, near the audio board. If there are so many inputs and outputs that some have to cross an ac power line, they should cross it at right angles. Never run an audio lead parallel to a power lead, though if you must, you might get away with it if the leads are at least an inch apart. Even the regulated dc leads that run from the power supply board to the audio board can carry some noise, so be cautious with them, too. Shielded cable or twisted-pair wires, discussed in the switch-box project of Chapter 4, will further reduce any stray hum or noise that might be picked up by the audio leads.

You'll want to fuse the project, unless you don't mind buying a new transformer or other parts whenever you make a serious wiring error. A ½-amp fuse will be adequate for any of the projects in this book. The fuse is shown in Fig. 5-6, along with a switch and an LED power indicator. You might wish to omit the switch, as I often do, and use a set of switched outlets for your entire system.

Note the current-limiting resistor on the LED. It should be ½ watt. Without it, the LED will burn out. The optimum value varies with the voltage and the type of LED. For 36 volts peak, as supplied by the 24-volt center-tapped transformer shown here, 2.2 k is near optimum with most LEDs.

The transformer will be one of the most expensive components in your project. There is no point in buying one larger than you need, unless you are getting a surplus bargain. Two-hundred milliamps will power any of the projects in this book. If you wish to power several projects from one supply, then use a one-amp transformer, fuse, and bridge rectifier.

———————————————————————REFERENCES———————————————————————

Staff of the American Radio Relay League, *The Radio Amateur's Handbook*. Newington, CT: The American Radio Relay League, Inc., 1979 (updated yearly).

6
Preamps and Amplifiers

Every audio system has a preamp and an amplifier, though they might share the same cabinet and a single power supply. While good sound can be had with an integrated unit, separate components offer greater flexibility and a chance to upgrade to the latest technology sooner and for less money than might otherwise be possible. Recent progress in tuner technology has been so rapid that a unit is often superseded as soon as it reaches the marketplace. Buying a separate tuner is more economical than replacing an entire receiver.

Separating the preamp from the amplifier can reduce noise and also reduce the modulation that peak power demand will impose on the power supply, and hence on the sound, of low-level signals in the preamplifier. The cost, however, may discourage you if you are not well-heeled. Most preamps cost more than a low-power receiver, and some cost thousands of dollars. Kits can save money, but there are not many kits available. Haffler is one company that still makes economical preamp kits of good quality. Such a kit will give you a slick, silk-screened front panel. If you want to build a kit from parts, you will need to have very neat handwriting in order to hand-letter a front panel so that it looks professional. Otherwise, if you don't mind a home-made look, it is still possible to save quite a few dollars and build your own preamp from scratch. (In some circles there is a certain prestige to obviously home-made equipment.) If you do decide to build your own preamp, you can still use your present integrated unit for an amplifier and/or an FM signal source.

Building your own power amp is a very good way to save money; a 100 watt amp will cost at least 500 dollars, while a 100 watt kit would cost over 300 dollars. I have built 100 watt stereo amps from parts for under 100 dollars. When you need two or three stereo amps for bi- or tri-amping, the savings add up. This chapter will discuss the workings of a representative amplifier.

A PASSIVE PREAMPLIFIER

A preamplifier performs two functions: switching between signal sources, and control of the signal level. The switch box discussed in Chapter 4 will perform the switching function. Except for the phonograph, all modern signal sources are sufficiently strong to drive an amplifier without additional amplification. By merely adding an attenuating potentiometer to the switch box, you can make a passive preamplifier. If you want to use a record player, a phono preamp will be necessary, but a passive preamp will handle all other signal sources. This is the purist's ultimate preamp: an old saying in audio defines the ideal amplifier as a straight wire with gain. Because gain for high-level signal sources isn't needed, the circuit can consist of nothing but wire. The purist's reasoning is that more circuitry just degrades the signal, despite the other advantages it might bestow. If you build the passive preamp using hermetically sealed switches with silver contacts, you will truly have the purist's ultimate preamp. Lower quality switches, of course, would add noise and distortion, due to dirt getting in the contacts, and the inherent resistance in base metal switch contacts. Even so, an inexpensive switch such as the double-ganged, six-pole switch sold by Radio Shack, will give reasonably good performance in a closed box. The wipers on their switch are self-cleaning and remove corrosion with use.

The schematic for the passive preamp is shown in Fig. 6-1, and the parts list in Table 6-1. The potentiometer should be a 10 kilohm, dual-ganged unit. Higher resistance values can cause frequency-response problems with some amplifiers and should be avoided.

While there is no balance control, when was the last time you used one? In the early

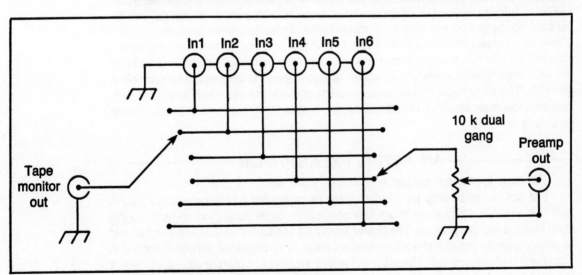

Fig. 6-1. Passive preamp left channel (right channel is identical).

Table 6-1. Passive Preamplifier Parts List.

All parts for passive preamp, plus:

Quantity	Item
4	2.4 k resistors
2	4.7 k resistors
1	10 k, linear taper pot for balance control
1	TL072 op amp
1	IC socket
1	IC board (e.g., Radio Shack #276-159)
1	Power supply

days of stereo, a balance control was necessary with many recordings. It is no longer necessary, for engineers have learned to mix for stereo. Some people claim the control is needed if the listening position is much closer to one speaker than to the other. If this is the case, rearrange your furniture: the time delay between speakers that are so asymmetrically placed from the listener as to require different level adjustments will interfere with stereo imaging. Perhaps the market demands a balance control on a commercial product, but many people don't need it and never use one.

If you must have separate level control for both channels, consider using two pots instead of a double-ganged one. This will increase separation, and despite the inconvenience, it isn't that hard to adjust two level controls, with less error than the inevitable mistracking that occurs with many ganged pots. Some audiophile preamps use such a dual-mono arrangement, actually using two mono preamps in two different cases, claiming the sacrifice in convenience is worth the sonic benefits. With CDs, I find that any such sonic benefits are nearly inaudible, though it seems to help with vinyl recordings and FM. The advantages of dual mono construction are greater when amplification is involved, because amplifier circuits allow for a greater degree of crosstalk, unless rigorously isolated.

AN ACTIVE PREAMPLIFIER

The parts list for this project is shown in Table 6-2.

You can use an op amp for a buffer stage to implement a balance control. This is shown in Fig. 6-2. Of course you are now routing the signal through an op amp, so this is no longer a passive preamp. The power supply for the buffer op amp can also be used to power a phono preamp and a tone control stage. The regulated supply described in Chapter 5 is recommended. Mounting the power supply in a separate case might result in lower noise, but is not necessary for good performance. When the balance control

Table 6-2. Active Preamplifier with Balance Control Parts List.

Amplifier Parts List.

Q1a,Q1b 2SC1583
Q2a,Q2b 2SA798
Q3 . . . . 2N4037
Q4 . . . . 2N3053
Q5,Q6 . . . . 2SD235 or T3228
Q8 . . . . 2SA616 or T3223
Q9,Q10 . . . . MJ15003
Q11,Q12 . . . . MJ15004

D1,D2 . . . . 1N914

C1 . . . . 180pF
C2 . . . . 3.3μF
C3 . . . . 47μF
C4,C5,C6 . . . . 0.1μF
C7 . . . . 56pF
C8 . . . . 1000μF
C9 . . . . 0.047μF

R1,R2,R16 . . . . 10K
R3,R5,R6 . . . . 3.3K
R4 . . . . 33K
R7,R8,R19 . . . . 56K
R9 . . . . 220 ohm
R10,R11 . . . . 100 ohm
R12,R18 . . . . 10 ohm
R13,R17 . . . . 390 ohm
R14 . . . . 2.7 K
R15 . . . . 820 ohm
R20 . . . . 120 ohm
R21,R22,
R23,R24 . . . . 0.25 ohm 3 watt
R25 . . . . 10 ohm 1 watt

VR1,VR2 . . . . 500 ohm, ¼ watt

L1 . . . . 12 turns #18 wire

is not centered, there will be appreciable dc offset voltages at the op amps' outputs, so a capacitor should be used to block dc offset. No output capacitor is shown; it is assumed that the power amplifier is ac coupled, that is, it has a buffer capacitor at the input. If your amplifier does not have an input capacitor, use the largest plastic film capacitor you can find at the output of the preamp to block the dc offset.

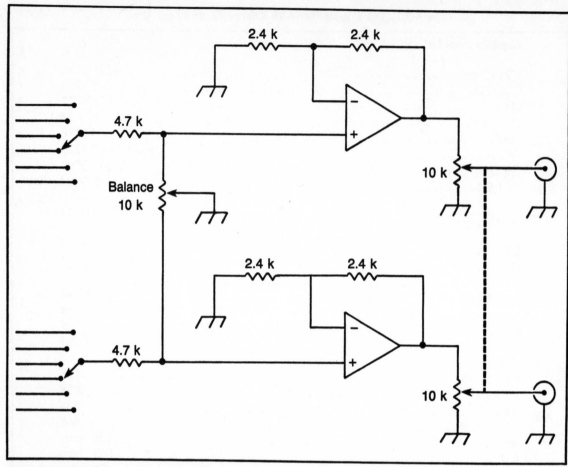

Fig. 6-2. Preamplifier with balance control.

While purists sneer at tone controls, they do make some program material more listenable, and can compensate for weakness in a speaker system at one end or the other of the spectrum. A graphic equalizer is better than tone controls for this purpose, but not everyone has or can afford one. My current preamp has no tone controls. Its predecessor had such controls, and a switch to bypass them. I found I always kept the tone controls switched out of the circuit. Now, even though I have a very sophisticated graphic equalizer, I seldom use it. Still, an occasional recording is much improved by its use.

Figure 6-3 shows how to add tone controls to the preamp. The parts list is shown in Table 6-3. Please note that the input to the tone control stage must be a low-impedance source, such as another op amp. The buffer for the balance control meets this need. Also, this circuit inverts the signal. If you wish to maintain correct polarity of the signal, you should add an inverting op amp after IC2. The audibility of polarity inversion is controversial; experiments indicate it is audible with certain test signals, but it does not seem to be readily detected by most listeners on musical material. With tone controls

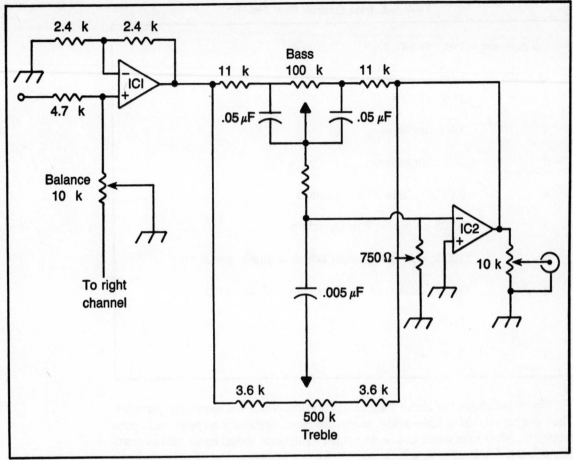

Fig. 6-3. Preamplifier with tone and balance controls.

in use, the added phase shift probably makes it even less audible. (If you are using tone controls, it seems odd to be worrying about the signal's polarity.)

As with the balance control circuit, a coupling capacitor will be needed at the preamp's output if the amp you are using does not have an input capacitor.

A PHONO PREAMPLIFIER

Most people have a sizeable number of vinyl recordings, and still require the capability to play them. Separate phono preamps are made: Radio Shack has always carried one. You can connect such a unit between your phono cartridge and one of the inputs to the preamp. As an alternative, building a phono preamp is not that difficult. If you are incorporating balance and tone controls into your preamp, you already have a power supply available for the op amps. Perhaps the most difficult part of the undertaking is finding the precision capacitors in the required values, which are seldom available off-the-shelf in small quantities.

Table 6-3. Tone Controls Parts List.

All parts for active preamp, plus:

Quantity	Item
6	11 k resistors
4	3.6 k resistors
2	750 ohm resistors
4	0.05 μF plastic film capacitors
2	0.005 μF plastic film capacitors
1	100 k, dual-gang, linear pot (or 2 single gang)
1	500 k, dual-gang, linear pot (or 2 single gang)
1	TL072 op amp
1	IC socket

Figure 6-4 shows the circuit for a phono preamp. Table 6-4 shows the parts list. The capacitors should be high-quality, plastic-film types, preferably polystyrene or polypropylene. Silver mica would also be acceptable. Tolerance should be as tight as possible, at worst 5% for the capacitors, and 1% for the resistors. The 20-μF capacitor's function is to limit gain at low frequencies. Perfectionists will want to bypass it with a 1 μF plastic film capacitor. (This is done by putting the plastic film capacitor parallel to the electrolytic.) The function of this circuit is two-fold: first, to provide 40 dB gain, and second, to provide RIAA equalization. The standard RIAA playback curve is plotted in Fig. 6-5. The high frequencies are boosted during recording, so the corresponding high frequency cut during playback results in a flat response, and also reduces the surface noise that is a major defect with this sort of recording. The bass is cut during recording. If this were not done, the excursion of the groove walls would pop the stylus right out of the groove for high-level bass signals. The required bass boost for flat response is provided by this circuit.

Other preamp and tone control circuits can be adapted from those found in *How to Design and Build Audio Amplifiers, Including Digital Circuits*—2nd Edition, #1206, published by TAB Books.

AMPLIFIERS

If you already have a perfectly good amplifier, you might want to skip this section, but don't. You will need two or three amps if you decide to biamp or triamp your system

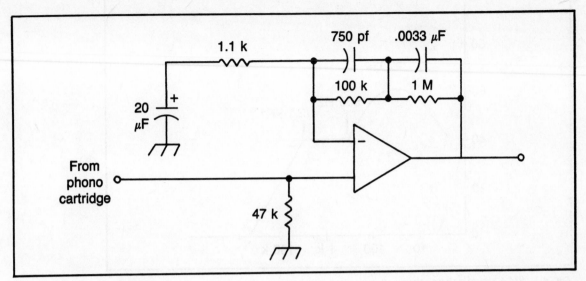

Fig. 6-4. Phono preamplifier.

with one of the circuits to be described in Chapter 9. Understanding how an amp works should contribute to your pleasure in building a kit, and will help in choosing a unit should you find a good buy in an assembled amplifier. Used amps are generally trouble-free and can be expected to give good service. After all, the perfect machine, by definition, has no moving parts, and the amplifier fits that description. If the unit is working, it can be expected to continue working, unless subject to abuse. (There are exceptions; some

Table 6-4. Phono Preamplifier Parts List.

Quantity	Item
1	TL072 op amp
2	47 k resistors
2	1.1 k resistors
2	100 k resistors
2	1 meg resistors
2	750 pF capacitors, plastic film or silver mica
2	0.0033 capacitors, plastic film

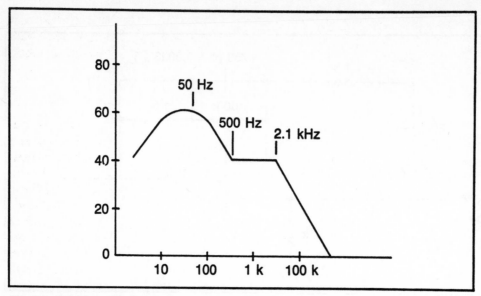

Fig. 6-5. RIAA equalization curve.

amps will blow their output transistors regularly, due to a faulty component in an earlier stage. This sort of condition is fortunately uncommon.)

You can build a kit; these are available in two forms. The first type's sole surviving representative seems to be Haffler. This company makes very good units that can stand on their own merits. They give the amateur a chance to build first-rate equipment. My only quarrel with this approach to kit building is that one is not so much building the unit as assembling it. The circuit boards are already stuffed and soldered. One merely mounts the power supply, puts boards and jacks on the chassis, wires them together, and plugs it in. Guaranteed to work 99.9% of the time. If you are such a complete klutz as to flub the job, the Haffler Company will fix it, at no charge if the defect was their fault.

The second type of kit is riskier. Some oriental companies supply a PC board, a bag of components, and a schematic. Any instructions are in Chinese, or Korean and broken English. You are on your own after that. Transformer and case are extra. With some experience, these kits are not that risky, and the price is very low, on the order of fifty cents per watt. The suppliers for these units constantly change, and the best way to locate them is to scan the ads in the back of electronics hobby magazines.

Another approach is to use modules. These are hybrid units containing integrated circuits and power transistors, and they must be mounted on heat sinks. The connections on the modules are typically for input, output, power-supply rails, and feedback path. With a power supply, a couple of capacitors, a coil and a heat sink, one has an amplifier. ILF is one manufacturer whose modules are distributed in this country. Replacement modules for Japanese amplifiers, in power ratings from 15 to 100 watts, are available from TV-radio repair store suppliers. For a nominal fee of 25 cents, they will also sell you an application sheet that will allow you to build an amplifier. The cost for a 100-watt module can be as low as $30.

Generally, what one looks for in an amp is enough power for the job at hand. An amplifier for a tweeter might be over-powered at 40 watts, while a subwoofer can need as much as 400 watts to reproduce an organ's lowest tones. An amp rated at 200 watts at eight ohms might not deliver enough current to drive a four ohm woofer, though usually 100 watts is enough for any likely situation.

A TYPICAL AMPLIFIER

The best way to become familiar with an amplifier's workings is to examine one. Figure 6-6 is a circuit used by the Tung Yung Electrical Company. It is billed as a "100-watt, pure class-A power amp." The unit can put out 100 watts at eight ohms, but only with the right power supply. Using a cheaper transformer could lower the output to 60 watts. Neither is the unit truly class-A, though it uses a clever bias circuit that produces almost the same result. It should be possible to put together a 100-watt stereo amp from this kit at a cost of between 120 and 150 dollars. (The current version of this amplifier is available from Mark V Electronics and incorporates a number of circuit improvements. The current version of the amplifier uses dc input coupling and newer versions of the transistors. See the Appendix for details.) Table 6-1 lists the parts.

Let us begin at the beginning and follow a signal through the amplifier. C1 and R3 form a filter to keep rf out of the amp. (If you live near a commercial transmitter or have a ham for a neighbor, their signals could otherwise overload the input transistors, whose frequency response extends to several megahertz.) R3 and R4 set the input impedance at 36 k, and C3 provides an ac return to ground for the input signal. R1, R2, VR1, and the two diodes provide a voltage to compensate for dc offset, as well as a bias voltage for the input transistors. Remember, the voltage drop across a forward-biased diode is 0.7 volts. Thus, the drop across potentiometer VR1 is 1.4 volts, and R1 and R2 assure that the voltage off the wiper will range between plus and minus 0.7 volts. This pot will be adjusted for minimum output voltage when there is no input signal.

The input transistors, Q1 and Q2, are super-beta bipolars. This means they are capable of very high gain. They each consist of two transistors on a common substrate, for purposes of temperature tracking and characteristic matching. It is possible to use two transistors, such as a pair of 2SC1313y's for Q1, and 2SA726y's for Q2, but the pairs should be matched in their characteristics.

Note that Q1 and Q2 form symmetrical circuits. This symmetry greatly reduces harmonic distortion. While it's possible to build an amplifier with only one differential pair, relying on feedback alone to lower distortion, a dual differential pair inherently produces less harmonic distortion.

A Differential Pair

The workings of a differential pair deserve an explanation. In function it is similar to an op amp in that there are two input points, inverting and noninverting, but there are also two output points, one inverting, the other noninverting. R7 acts as a current source because it is large relative to R5 and R10. The current is divided between the two transistors, but must always sum to the same current as is flowing through R7. Thus, an input signal on the base of Q1a will produce an inverted but amplified signal at the collector of Q1a, but the feedback signal applied at the base of Q1b will not be

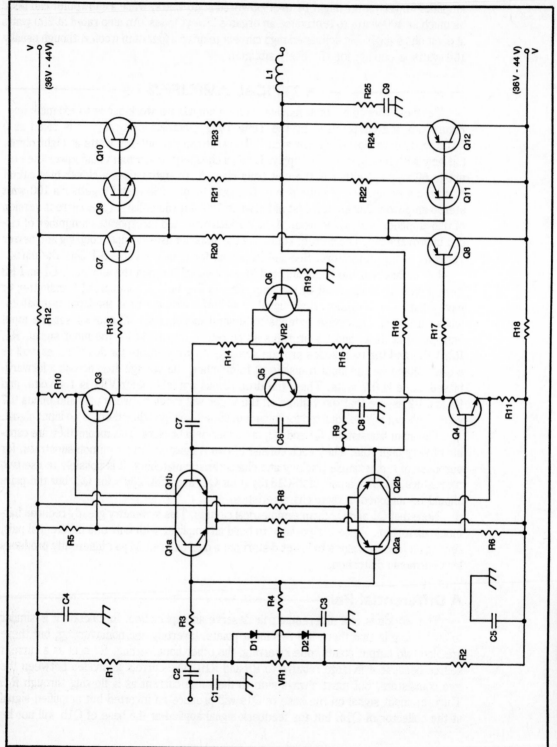

Fig. 6-6. An amplifier circuit.

inverted when it is summed with the input signal at the collector of Q1a. (It is also possible to take a signal of opposite polarity to that at the Q1a collector from the Q1b collector, although that is not done here.) Because the two transistors are each supplying an amount of current that is complementary to the other's current, they force each other to be more linear, reducing distortion. Because noise will often be picked up on both the negative and positive inputs, it will cancel out. This is known as *common-mode noise rejection*.

One possible improvement would be to substitute a true current source for R7. This could be done with a transistor and a few resistors, and would make this stage even more linear. Evidently, the designers decided the theoretical improvement in performance would not be worth the cost.

The Class-A Driver Stage

Q3 and Q4 are both class-A drivers, in that they operate in their linear range, and they never shut off. They provide most of the voltage gain in the amp, but very little power gain, for the current is relatively low. These transistors are operating in *push-pull* fashion, i.e., they are of opposite polarity, so one "pushes" while the other "pulls." In response to a signal of the same polarity, one will tend to pass more current while the other passes less. Because their polarities are different, the resulting output signal is the same. Because the transistors are operated in a common-collector configuration, they invert the signal. Combined with the inversion in the differential input stage, this results in a signal of correct polarity to feed the next and final stage.

Q3 and Q4 will run quite hot and will need to be adequately heat-sinked. The voltage gain of this stage will be very high. But despite this gain, more current is needed to drive a loudspeaker.

The Emitter-Follower Output Stage

Q9 and Q10 operate in parallel; R21 and R22 assure that current will be equally divided between them, or else one might hog all the current and destroy itself. Q7 provides enough current gain to supply the current needed by the base circuit of the final output pair. This configuration, with one emitter follower feeding another (or others), is known as a *Darlington pair*.

Q11, Q12, and Q8 are symmetrical to the npn output transistors but are opposite in polarity. Some amps use all npn output transistors in a quasi-complementary symmetry configuration, although with the many complementary pairs of npn and pnp power transistors now available at reasonable cost, this design has fallen out of favor. Most audiophiles consider quasi-comp amps inferior because the two halves of the amp are not truly symmetrical, and so can be expected to produce nonlinearities, or distortion. Yet most complementary pairs are not truly symmetrical, having some differences in operating characteristics. This is especially true of power VFETs. Perhaps the reputation of the quasi-complementary symmetrical amp has been unjustly tarnished.

The Bias Network

If a high enough bias voltage were present at the base of Q7 (and Q8) to assure that these transistors never shut off, even during peak negative (or positive) voltage swings by the input signal, the output transistors would get very hot. They might even burn out. In any case, the amp could only put out about 10 watts. This would be class-A operation. Distortion would be low, but power would be limited. Without any bias, the base voltages would be identical on Q7 and Q8, and both output halves would be off during low-signal excursions. The resulting crossover distortion (which occurs as the signal crosses over the zero voltage point) would make the amp unlistenable. The solution adopted by most designers is to use the so-called class-AB bias circuit; enough of a voltage difference is provided between the bases of Q7 and Q8 so that one transistor doesn't shut off until the other one is turned on and delivering power. Negative feedback is used to eliminate any nonlinearities or noise produced by the switching of the output transistors. Such an amp actually runs class-A at very low output levels. Some designers have reasoned that the switching noise adds to distortion, and have sought to eliminate it, as is done here.

Q5 provides the bias for the output stage. VR2 sets the amount of bias. If Q6 were not there, this would be a standard class-AB bias network. But Q6 changes the base voltage on Q5 with changes in the signal level, so that the amount of bias varies just enough to keep both Q7 and Q8 on at all times, albeit at very low current levels. Overall negative feedback is used to reduce any nonlinearities this biasing scheme might introduce.

Biasing schemes of this sort go by different names that include the term "class A," such as nonswitching class A. Despite the name, this is not really class A. How does it sound? With Q6 removed from the circuit, VR2 can adjust the bias level for class-AB operation. It is then possible to compare class AB and pseudo-class A. I have done so and believe that there is an audible improvement in the nonswitching circuit. Measurements made by the manufacturers promoting nonswitching amps also show less high-order harmonic distortion than class-AB operation.

The Feedback Network

R16, R9, and C8 are the feedback network. They "feed back" the amp's output to the negative inputs of the differential input pairs. The ratio of R16 to R9 determines the overall amplifier gain. C8 changes this ratio at low frequencies, so that there is 100% feedback at dc. If this were not done, slight dc offsets could put your speaker cones in your lap, for the amp's output is direct coupled.

L1 assures some resistance at high frequencies. This coil can be made from 12 turns of 18-gauge wire wound about a pencil, spread over a distance of one inch. (Remove the pencil when finished winding.) R25 and C9 assure that resistance will not be too high. These components comprise a "Zobel" network. Without the Zobel network, the amp might become unstable, oscillating at high frequencies and destroying the output transistors. Some VFET amps don't require such a network, but its use is universal with bipolar output transistors.

The Power Supply

Figure 6-7 is the manufacturer's recommended power supply. Note that a range of values is shown for the transformer voltage and current, as well as for the filter capacitors. Let us start with the filter capacitors.

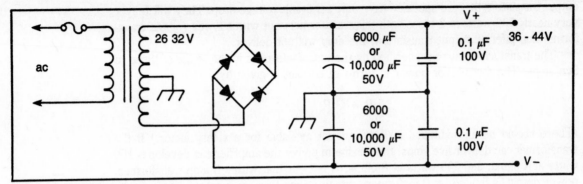

Fig. 6-7. Amplifier power supply.

Although 6000 μF is adequate, larger values will allow quieter operation and more dynamic power reserve. This is because the larger the capacitor, the more charge it can store, and so the more power it will deliver before it discharges. Note that two ranges of voltage are given: one for the power transformer, and another following the filter capacitors. The transformer output voltage represents the rms (root mean square) voltage delivered by the transformer, and the second set of voltages is the peak voltage, which the capacitors maintain under no-load conditions. The ratio between these two values is approximately 1.4 to 1. The capacitors must be rated at least five volts greater than this peak. Fifty volts will be adequate. Higher voltage ratings will work but tend to be more expensive. You could use larger capacitors than 10,000 μF, but be warned—when power is first applied—the capacitors look like a short to the rectifier and the transformer. They will briefly try to deliver a huge amount of current to the capacitors. If the capacitors are too large, these parts could burn out before the load diminished. For this reason, a 400-volt bridge rectifier rated at 25 amps is recommended, though a smaller value could be used. The usual recommendation is that the rectifier voltage be twice the maximum voltage difference encountered in the circuit, which in this case is about 90 volts; in theory a 200-volt rectifier, rated at twice the amp's peak current, could be used. Using the larger rectifier will prevent problems that could arise due to inadequate ventilation and heat dissipation for the rectifier. If you plan to use capacitors much larger than 12,000 μF, you should provide some means of current limiting during turn-on. This is usually done with low-ohmage, high-wattage resistors and relays on both supply rails to bypass the resistors after the capacitor is charged. Bypass capacitors should be used for the power supply, just as one uses for op amps. Mount 0.1 μF plastic film caps on the amps's PC board, from the positive and negative voltage leads to ground.

The transformer is the key to how much continuous power the amp will be able to deliver into a load. The formula for power in terms of voltage is:

$$P = V^2 / R$$

where V is the voltage, and R the resistance of the load. The distributer supplied a 30-0-30 volt transformer (60 volts center tapped) for this kit. For an 8-ohm speaker, the most continuous power that could be available would be 112.5 volts. In real life, the output transistors would not deliver the full voltage. Most output transistors will have a voltage drop of 5 volts; the amp then delivers only about 80 watts at 8 ohms. The Motorola output transistors that are specified have only a 2.5-volt voltage drop. They will deliver very nearly 100 watts at 8 ohms with this transformer; but with a lower voltage transformer and inferior output transistors, the amp will not deliver.

The transformer current specified by the manufacturer is in the range of three to five amps. The formula for power in terms of current is given by:

$$P = I^2 R$$

(There should be an additional 20% of current available for a safety factor.) If the transformer can deliver five amps, the maximum power the amplifier can develop is 100 watts at 4 ohms, and 200 watts at 8 ohms. It is clear that with a 5 amp transformer, power output is limited by transformer voltage rather than by current.

Should the transformer only deliver three amps, then maximum power is limited to 36 watts at 4 ohms, and 72 watts at 8 ohms. The lesson here is that the proper transformer is critical to an amplifier's performance. Mark V supplies a transformer rated at 6 amps at 30 volts.

Attempting to increase the power output by using a larger transformer is not a good idea. You will be exceeding the output transistors' power rating. Note that you will need a separate 5-amp transformer and power supply for each channel for full power output from both channels simultaneously. Dedicated audiophiles consider this to be a superior arrangement in any case. If you can find a single 8- or 10-amp transformer for both channels, fuse both the positive and negative supply rails with 5-amp fuses; this will protect the output transistors against a premature burial. These fuses are a good idea in any case.

It is also a good idea to fuse the speaker line with a 2-amp fuse. The fuse will blow slowly enough so that it will pass higher transient currents, but it will heat up under repeated abuse and blow out before your speaker's voice coils overheat. The golden-eared crowd maintains that the tiny amount of resistance offered by a fuse degrades the sound and raises a speaker's effective Q. Perhaps, but I have seen an unfused speaker catch fire when an output transistor shorted out. The cone was charred, and the plastic fabric grill cloth burned and melted. This didn't sound good at all. Of course there are other methods than a fuse to protect a speaker, but none are so fail-safe and so inexpensive.

For those wishing to explore amplifier circuitry in more detail, as well as many other topics, *The Audio Amateur* magazine carries many articles on circuitry and project construction. If you send a stamped, self-addressed envelope, Edward Dell will be glad to send a list of available back issues and their contents.

REFERENCES

Dell, Edward T. Jr. (Ed.). *The Audio Amateur*, P.O. Box 576, Peterborough, NH 03458-0576.

Lenk, John D. *Handbook of Simplified Solid-State Circuit Design*. Englewood Cliffs, NJ: Prentice-Hall, Inc., 1978.

Phelps, Roland S. (Ed). *750 Practical Electronic Circuits*. Blue Ridge Summit PA: TAB Books, 1983.

7

Basic Op Amp Projects

T HE OP AMP CIRCUITS OF CHAPTER 3 CAN BE USED TO PERFORM MANY USEFUL FUNC-tions. With a few examples and a little practice, you should be able to combine these basic circuits to implement your own ideas. Here are some examples.

AMPLIFIER BRIDGING CIRCUIT

The simplest useful op amp circuit may well be the amplifier bridging circuit. If you have a stereo amp of moderate power, you can turn it into a high-power mono amp to drive a single subwoofer. A pair of stereo amps can become two high-power amps for a more powerful stereo system. The circuit can be implemented with a single op amp. The parts can be had for under $10, yet some manufacturers charge five and even ten times as much for this simple circuit.

A stereo amplifier can, in theory, be converted to a mono amp with up to four times the power of a single one of its channels. This is done by inverting the signal that is fed to one amp, then connecting the speaker so that its positive terminal connects to the noninverting amp's hot terminal, and the speaker's negative terminal connects to the inverting amp's hot terminal. A block diagram is shown in Fig. 7-1. This arrange-ment doubles the voltage that is available across the speaker. Recalling the formula given in Chapter 6, doubling the voltage will quadruple the power. If you have a 50-watt stereo amp, you can turn it into a 200-watt mono amp, but in practice this much power will seldom be available. The amp's current-handling capability will limit the bridged out-put. When an amp is bridged, one can usually expect twice as much power.

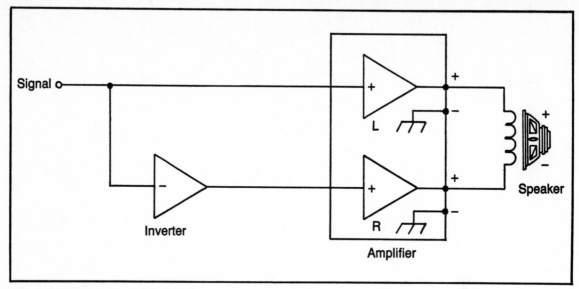

Fig. 7-1. Bridging circuit block diagram.

Caution: some amps will not function well when bridged. Any amp that cannot simultaneously handle two pairs of speakers in parallel is not a good candidate because this indicates limited current-sourcing ability. Many of the less expensive Japanese receivers are in this category. Some high-power amps are already bridged. A careful reading of your amp's owner's manual should tell you what you need to know. If the power output at four ohms is higher than at eight, go ahead and bridge. If the manual is not available, examine the amplifier's guts. Is the power transformer relatively large and solid looking? Are there more than two output transistors per channel? Are they mounted on a large and sturdy heatsink? Are they TO-3 devices? If the answer to most of these questions is yes, the amp will probably do well when bridged.

The bridging circuit is shown in Fig. 7-2, and the parts list in Table 7-1. The resistor values are not critical, but must be closely matched. One percent accuracy is recommended. Any value from 10 k to 100 k is fine, though the lower values will be very slightly quieter. R3 can be replaced by a piece of wire if your amp's inputs are capacitively coupled. If there is no blocking capacitor, you should use R3 to minimize the op amp offset voltage. Alternatively, use a nonpolarized blocking capacitor at the op amp's output. (Any value between 4.7 and 10 μF should be good.) The sort of capacitor sold for speaker crossovers will serve well, though you might want to hunt for plastic film caps in the requisite value. The exact value used is not critical, but it must be large enough to pass the lowest frequency of interest.

Once you've finished the circuit, connect the "out+" output to the amp's left channel input, and connect the "out−" output to the right channel input. Connect the speakers hot (+, or red) terminal to the amp's left channel hot terminal. Connect the speaker's ground, negative (−, or black) lead to the right channel's hot terminal. Connect a signal source and try it out, but proceed cautiously. If the amp shows signs of distress, proceed no further, and disconnect the bridging circuit. First listen at moderate levels, checking the output transistors and heatsinks for signs of overheating. If the heatsinks get

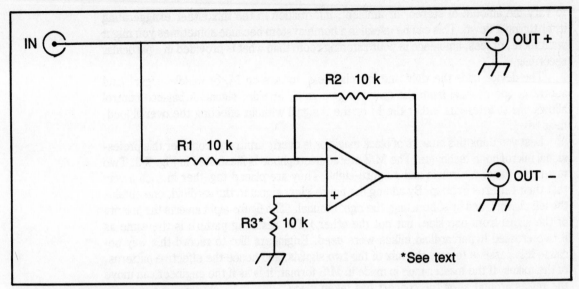

IN

R2 10 k

R1 10 k

OUT +

−
+

OUT −

R3* 10 k

*See text

Fig. 7-2. Bridging circuit schematic.

hot enough to boil water, you're in trouble. They might be warm, even uncomfortable to touch, but if this is normal in unbridged operation, this is okay.

A SHUFFLER

An English sound engineer once told me that the shuffler is a common device in English recording studios, though it doesn't seem to have made it to our side of the Atlantic. What the shuffler does is to "shuffle" a stereo signal, allowing an engineer

Table 7-1. Amplifier Bridging Circuit Parts List.

Quantity	Item
1	TL071 op amp
3	10 k resistors
3	Phono plugs
1	IC socket
1	IC board (e.g., Radio Shack #276-159)
1	Power supply
1	Case

to vary the amount of stereo, or ambient, information in the mix, either exaggerating it, or toning it down. This can be useful in a home system because sometimes you might want more, or less, ambience in your listening room than what is provided in a particular recording.

The device adds the right and left channels, to give an M, or middle, signal, and subtracts one channel from the other to give an S, or side, signal. A balance control allows one to attenuate either the M or the S signal without affecting the overall loudness level.

Lest you think this smacks of black magic or is overly arbitrary, consider this professional microphone technique: The M/S stereo microphone is illustrated in Fig. 7-3. Two mikes are used, a cardioid and a figure-eight. They are placed together in such a way that their patterns overlap. By adding the figure-eight signal to the cardioid, one obtains the left channel, and by subtracting, the right channel. (The figure-eight inverts the polarity of the signal from one side, but not the other.) The resulting pattern is the same as if two crossed hypercardioid mikes were used. Engineers like to record this way because it is possible to vary the mix of the two signals, and hence the effective patterns, of the mikes. If the master tape is made in M/S format, it is as if the engineer can move the mikes around after the concert has taken place.

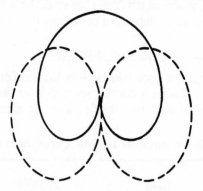

Cardioid and figure-8 microphone patterns can be electrically combined. . .

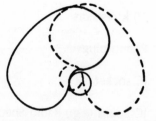

to give the same pattern as two crossed hypercardioide microphones

Fig. 7-3. M-S microphone technique. (A) Cardioid and figure-8 microphone patterns can be electrically combined . . . (B) to give the same pattern as two crossed hypercardioid microphones.

The shuffler allows you to do the same thing, but with any recording. Even though most recordings aren't made with M/S microphones or with crossed cardioids, this method still works. You can increase ambience on video sound tracks, making your surround sound decoder even more effective. A musically interesting but technically inept recording can be corrected. By including send and receive capability for the M/S signals, the stereo information can be processed separately from the mono information. Varying the frequency response of the two signals in different ways with a graphic equalizer allows for further enhancement of a recording's ambience, or greater precision in center stage imaging. One can even use the technique for FM noise reduction, as I explain in the next section.

The circuit is shown in Fig. 7-4, and the parts list in Table 7-2. ICI is an inverting, summing op amp. Its output is therefore $-(R+L)$, or $-M$, the "middle" signal. IC2 is a difference amplifier with unity gain. Its output is $(R+L)$, or S, the "side" signal. IC3 is an inverting summer, IC4 a difference amp. If the $-M$ and S signals were simply summed by IC3, its output would be 2L. Likewise with IC4; subtracting $-M$ from S would give 2R. R7, R8, and P1 conspire to reduce the signal levels by half when P1 is in its center position; the resistors combine with the pot to form voltage dividers that also raise the level of one signal as the other is reduced. This allows the overall level to remain reasonably constant even though the M or the S signal is attenuated. If you are having trouble following this explanation, then you should review Chapter 2 on op amps and actually work out the algebra involved.

The output capacitors may be omitted if the next device in the signal chain is capacitor coupled. If you use them, the exact value is not critical, though the larger they are, the better the base response. The exact cut-off point, of course, depends on the input impedance of the next stage, 4.7 μF should be more than adequate. Larger values are okay, but lower values might be fine with your equipment. The caps should be nonpolarized; electrolytics are acceptable, though plastic film are preferable.

If you are in the recording business, the uses for the shuffler are obvious. The home audio enthusiast who is not interested in surround sound might think the device is less useful. Don't reject it out of hand. It can liven up overly dry recordings, or sharpen up poorly mixed ones. And for FM noise reduction, it can work miracles.

HIGH BLEND FOR FM

You can reduce noise and interference on FM reception by blending only the high frequencies, allowing the lower ones to remain stereo. You can accomplish this with a single capacitor, or use the shuffler circuit for even better results. To understand why blending the highs reduces noise on FM, it's necessary to understand how FM stereo transmission works.

FM, of course, stands for frequency modulation. The carrier signal changes frequency with amplitude changes in the modulating signal. A mono signal with an upper limit of 15 kHz modulates, or changes the frequency, of its carrier, as many as 15,000 times a second. Although present-day FM is limited to a 15 kHz bandwidth, this is an arbitrary rather than a physical limit. An FM carrier could be modulated with a 100 kilohertz signal. In fact, in the early days of FM broadcasting, there was no defined upper limit to

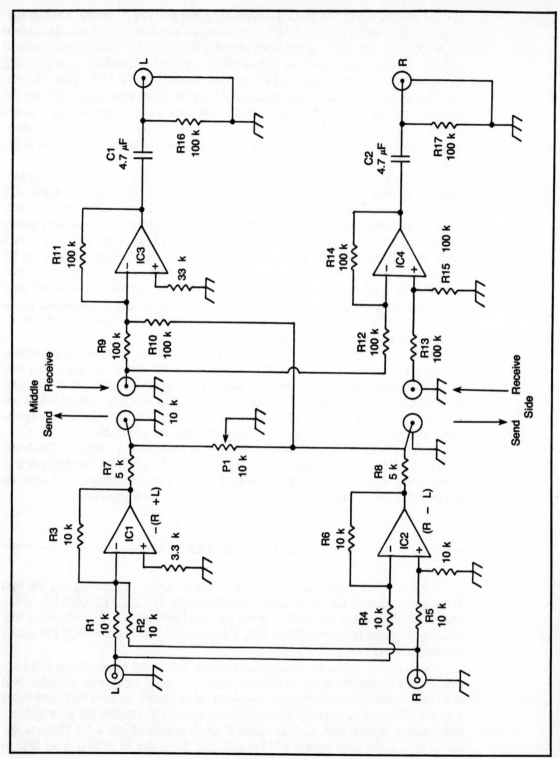

Fig. 7-4. Schematic for the shuffler.

Table 7-2. Shuffler Parts List.

Quantity	Item
7	10 k resistors
2	5 k resistors, or 2 pair 10 k, in parallel
10	100 k resistors, 1%
1	10 k, linear taper potentiometer
2	4.7 μF or greater non-polarized capacitors
1	TL074, or two TL072 op amps
8	Phono jacks
1	IC board (e.g., Radio Shack #276-159)
1	Case
—	Power supply

the modulating frequency. Live broadcasts then had more highs than the phonograph cartridges of that day could reproduce. Hi-fi enthusiasts considered FM to be the most perfect medium, for there were no mechanical parts between the mikes and the speakers. (A book by some of Son's engineers, *Digital Audio Technology*, states that FM recording techniques similar to those used for hi-fi VCRs, could produce recordings equal to, and even superior in some respects, to current digital techniques. This illustrates the possible quality of an FM signal.)

Then along came stereo. Since not many people can hear higher than 15 or 20 kHz, all that bandwidth was going to waste. The process known as multiplexing is now used to put the extra channel up beyond audibility. A second channel is transposed upward by 38 kHz for transmission. On reception, it is transposed down again into the audible range. To maintain compatibility with existing mono FM tuners, the FCC chose a system in which the main FM signal is (R+L), or mono. The multiplex signal is (R−L). This should sound familiar. As in the shuffler, the multiplexed signals are added and subtracted to obtain the right and left channels.

This description is an oversimplification. The actual multiplex signal is really an AM double side band (suppressed carrier) signal. Readers wishing to know more about FM multiplex should see William I. Orr's *Radio Handbook*.

Unfortunately, the multiplexed (R−L) signal is much more vulnerable to interference and multipath noise than the main signal. Things are further complicated by the fact that many stations practice "storecasting." This imposes another signal on the FM carrier, above 80 kHz. This SCA signal is a commercial service paid for by those who want uninterrupted music in their stores, elevators, or other commercial establishments. If the SCA signal is overmodulated, it interferes with the multiplex signal.

Because most of the interference, whether due to SCA or other sources, is with the multiplexed signal, one can usually get good mono reception even though the stereo signal is unpleasantly noisy. If you have a station in your area that is objectionably noisy in stereo, but sounds good in mono, a high blend technique can help. The degradation of the signal-to-noise ratio caused by these forms of interference grows progressively worse as frequency increases. If you blend only the highs, and leave the lows separated, the noise can be eliminated. Because most of the stereo information is carried by the portion of the signal below two or three kilohertz, you will hear music in stereo. The simplest implementation requires only a capacitor, and perhaps a switch, box, and connecting jacks. A more sophisticated approach is to use the shuffler, together with an active filter.

Single-Capacitor High Blend

A high blend circuit using a single capacitor is shown in Fig. 7-5. The parts list is shown in Table 7-3. The value of the capacitor depends on the input impedance of your preamp, and on how severe the interference is. Because the preamp's impedance level could be anywhere from a low of 10 kHz to as high as 100 kHz and noise severity varies, you will want to try several different capacitors in order to find a value that leaves the stereo effect intact yet reduces noise. The situation is complicated further because devices connected to your tape monitor loop(s) can lower the impedance. If your equipment configuration is stable, you may use a single capacitor after you've found a workable value by experimentation. I am constantly connecting and disconnecting various recorders to my preamp, so I chose to use a multiple pole switch I had in my parts bin, together with five capacitors, as shown in Fig. 7-6. You will want to use a non-shorting switch, also known as break-before-make. The switch I used is a two-gang, six-pole switch that

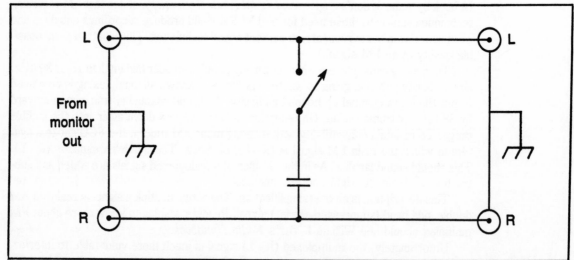

Fig. 7-5. Single capacitor high-blend circuit for FM noise reduction.

Quantity	Item
1	0.01 μF capacitor
1	0.022 μF capacitor
1	0.05 μF capacitor
1	0.1 μF capacitor
1	0.22 μF capacitor
1	Six-pole switch
4	Phono plugs
—	Case, hookup wire

Table 7-3. Passive High Blend for FM Parts List.

is carried by Radio Shack. (Catalog #275-1386.) Half the switch is unused. The sixth position is the "off" position. An "off" position is a necessity, otherwise all your signals will be high blended, degrading music from a compact disc or a vinyl album. Even if you elect to use a single capacitor, use a switch so that you can turn the high blend off.

You can cut inexpensive cables equipped with RCA plugs in half, and twist the center leads to either end of a capacitor to test how the circuit sounds, and to find out what value capacitor(s) you want to use. If you want to make the setup permanent, a small aluminum project box can hold the parts. The circuit can be placed between your tuner

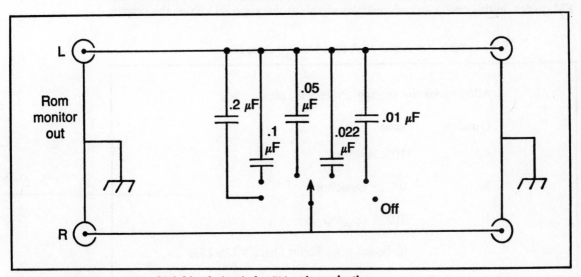

Fig. 7-6. Multiple capacitor high-blend circuit for FM noise reduction.

and preamp if you have separates. Otherwise, plug it into the tape-monitor-out jacks of your receiver. You will want to use the extra pair of RCA jacks shown in Fig. 7-6 to maintain monitor capability.

Using the Shuffler for High Blend

If you have built the shuffler and own a graphic equalizer, you can use the two for an active high-blend circuit. The parts list for this project is shown in Table 7-4. Simply route the signal from the point marked "S send" in Fig. 7-4 to the input of one channel of the graphic equalizer, and connect the equalizer's output to the point marked "S receive." Start with all sliders set at their midpoints. Start with the highest frequency, and gradually reduce its setting. Proceed similarly with subsequent bands, working down in frequency, until you have obtained the best possible balance between noise and a good stereo effect. This will probably occur with the 8-kHz control at minimum, and the 4-kHz control most, but not quite, all of the way down. If noise is severe, you might need to adjust the 2-kHz control, though separation will begin to degrade noticeably.

Even if you obtain good results this way, you might not want to dedicate your graphic equalizer to this function. You can build an active high-pass filter, with its cutoff frequency set to approximately 2.2 kHz, to replace the equalizer. Such a filter is shown in Fig. 7-7. You may use a dual op amp such as the TL072 for the filter, and leave the extra op amp unconnected, if a single op amp IC isn't available.

The filter's frequency is fixed at 2.2 kHz, and its attenuation rate is 12 dB per octave. It's possible to use a 10-kilohm double-ganged pot in combination with smaller input resistors (at least 1000 ohms) to vary the filter's cutoff frequency for greater high-frequency separation when interference is less severe.

Another FM Noise Reduction Technique

This section would be incomplete if it didn't mention another FM noise reduction technique that has been developed. The FMX method adds yet another signal to the FM carrier, in this case a second multiplex signal, at the same 38 kHz as the original

Table 7-4. Active High Blend for FM Parts List.

All parts for the shuffler (Project 9), plus:

Quantity	Item
4	10 k resistors
3	0.1 μF capacitors
1	TL071 op amp
1	IC board (e.g., Radio Shack #276-159)

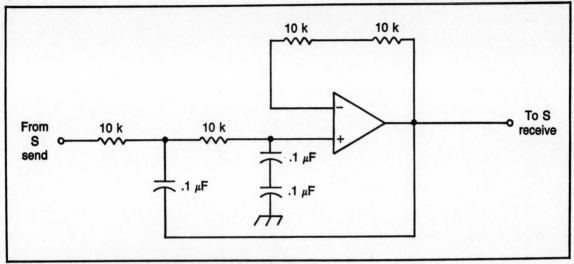

Fig. 7-7. Filter for shuffler high-blend FM noise reduction.

multiplex signal, but in phase quadrature, i.e., 90 degrees out of phase to the original multiplex signal. This enables the two signals to be separately detected. The FMX signal undergoes a compression process in which the entire signal is boosted to the maximum level the medium can carry. The original multiplex signal is used to determine how much decompression to apply to restore the FMX signal to its proper level. When compression is applied, the noise level is also suppressed. I do not know if this feat of technical wizardry is inaudible, but it is quiet.

For FMX to work, you need two things: a receiver equipped with FMX circuitry, and an FM station that transmits an FMX signal. If you don't want to invest in a new tuner, FMX is no help, though it won't hurt, because an FMX signal is compatible with ordinary multiplex stereo. FM stations seem eager to adopt the method because it increases the range of their stereo coverage. Because the circuitry can be incorporated on relatively inexpensive chips, manufacturers should be able to use it at little cost. It might prove more successful than Dolby® FM, which never caught on, and which suffered from compatibility problems.

I doubt if marginal FMX reception can be improved with the high blend circuit. It seems unlikely, though not impossible.

REFERENCES

Orr, William I., *Radio Handbook,* 22nd ed. Indianapolis, IN: Howard W. Sams & Co., 1981.

Nakamura, H., Doi, T., Fukuda, J., and Iga, P. *Digital Audio Technology.* Blue Ridge Summit, PA: TAB Books Inc., 1983.

8

Active Filters

A FILTER, AS THE NAME IMPLIES, REMOVES SOME PART OF A SIGNAL. FILTERS CAN BE be high-pass, removing the lows, or low-pass, removing the highs. They can be bandpass or band-reject. A notch filter is a band-reject filter with a very narrow reject band.

Passive filters are made with resistors, capacitors, and inductors. Where a filter must handle power, as in loudspeaker crossover networks, certain problems become evident. Inductors saturate when called upon to handle high current, causing distortion. Both capacitors and inductors interact with a speaker system's voice coils in undesirable ways. As a result they can pass a significant signal outside their intended passband, degrading the sound, if not damaging the speakers.

Even in low-level circuits, passive filters have problems. If a sharp rate of cutoff is desired, the passive filter will have an insertion loss, and additional amplification will be required. Inductors pick up hum and other electronic noise. In a low-level signal subject to further amplification, this can be a disaster.

Active filters eliminate these problems, at the cost of an op amp or two. Much sharper rates of cutoff become practical than with passive filters. There are some tradeoffs when replacing loudspeaker crossovers with active filters; an extra amplifier will be required, because separate signal paths are needed after the active crossover stage. Some audiophiles claim that active filters using feedback introduce distortion and prefer to use simple first-order passive filters. I believe that the distortion introduced by a properly designed active filter will be inaudible and will be far less deleterious than the sorts of distortion introduced by passive filters and by the constraints imposed by using such filters.

This chapter will enable the reader to design and build a number of useful and technically sophisticated active filters.

FILTER ORDER AND Q

Two parameters are used to describe a filter's response: order and Q. A filter's *order* is a measure of the ultimate rate of attenuation. A first-order filter has a slow rate of attenuation—six dB per octave. A second-order filter's attenuation is more respectable at 12 dB per octave. Each increase in order results in another 6 dB per octave attenuation. Eighteen dB per octave would be characteristic of a third-order filter; a ninth-order filter would have an attenuation of 54 dB per octave.

Q is related to the sharpness of the filter's cutoff near the resonant frequency, where the filter action begins to take effect. The higher the Q, the sharper the cutoff rate where the filter first begins to take effect. There is a price for this initially sharper rate of attenuation. For high Q's, there will be a bump in the filter's response curve, which degrades performance in audio applications. There will also be a significant amount of ringing with high-Q filters; such a filter will resonate like a bell. The audibility of this resonance depends on the filter's frequency and on room acoustics.

Q is sometimes expressed by its inverse: damping is signified by the letter "d." Low damping is equivalent to high Q. Figure 8-1 illustrates the frequency response curves of a first-order filter, and of second-order filters with different damping factors.

BASIC FILTER CIRCUITS

A capacitor and a resistor form the simplest filter, a passive first-order filter. The low-pass version is illustrated in Fig. 8-2. Its cutoff frequency is given by the equation:

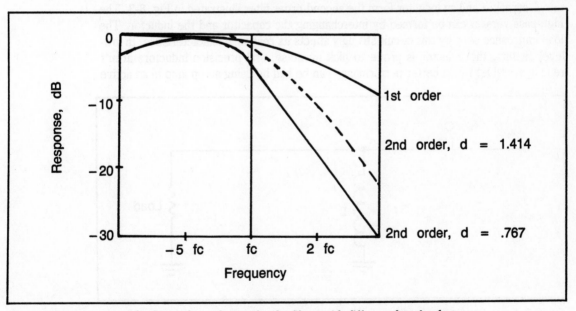

Fig. 8-1. Response curves for first-order and second-order filters with different damping factors.

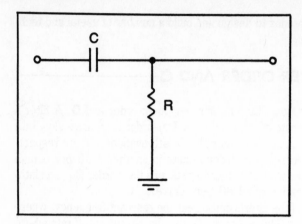

Fig. 8-2. First-order passive filter.

$$f_c = 1/(2\pi RC)$$

where:

$\pi = 3.14$
R = resistance of the resistor in ohms
C = capacitance in farads

The slope of the response curve well above the cutoff frequency is -6 dB per octave; amplitude is halved for every doubling in frequency. A high-pass filter can be made by reversing the positions of the resistor and the capacitor. A unity-gain voltage follower may be used after this filter to buffer its output, so that the impedance of a succeeding stage does not interfere with its response characteristics.

A capacitor and an inductor form the second-order filter illustrated in Fig. 8-3. The high-pass version can be formed by interchanging the capacitor and the inductor. The load impedance seen by this circuit strongly affects its response characteristics. In low-level circuits, the inductor is prone to pick up noise, and precision inductors aren't readily available. Much better performance can be had by using an op amp in an active

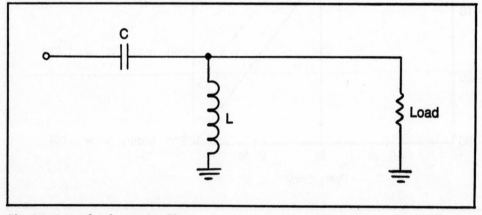

Fig. 8-3. Second-order passive filter.

filter circuit. A unity-gain, Sallen-Key low-pass filter is shown in Fig. 8-4. The cutoff frequency is given by:

$$f_c = 1/(2\pi RC)$$

This is the same formula as for the first-order filter, but none of the capacitors have a value of "C" farads. Instead, the ratio of the capacitors' values to "C" is determined by the damping factor, "d." For a Butterworth, or maximally flat filter, d = 1.414. It works out that the capacitor on the right in Fig. 8-4 must be half the size of the one on the left. The resistor labeled 2R is non-critical, and is usually replaced by a short; where minimum offset voltage is desired, this resistor's value should be twice that of the frequency setting resistors.

Because there is no dc path to ground at the positive input of the op amp, one must be provided by the preceding stage, either by feeding this circuit from another op amp, or by putting a resistor one-fifth (or less) the value of R between the input node and ground. This is the same type of filter that was used in Chapter 7 for the FM noise-reduction circuit.

The high-pass version of this circuit is shown in Fig. 8-5. The cutoff frequency is determined just as for the low-pass filter. This time it is the ratio of the resistors that determines the damping factor. For a maximally flat filter with a damping factor of 1.414, the resistor on the right should be twice the value of the one on the left. The feedback resistor is again non-critical, and can be replaced by a short.

The low-pass unity-gain filter may be tuned by using a double-ganged pot for the input resistors; the high-pass filter cannot be tuned easily. Obtaining capacitors in the required ratio is not all that easy for the low-pass filter. Another version of the Sallen-Key circuit sets the damping independently of the frequency, but the gain is no longer

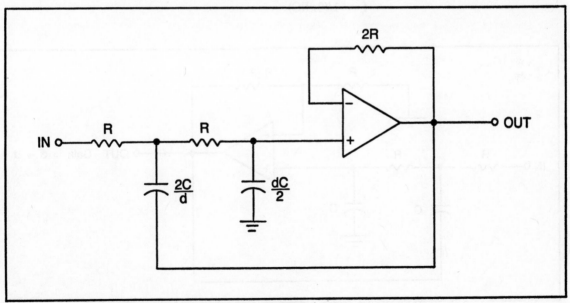

Fig. 8-4. Second-order unity-gain Sallen-Key low-pass filter.

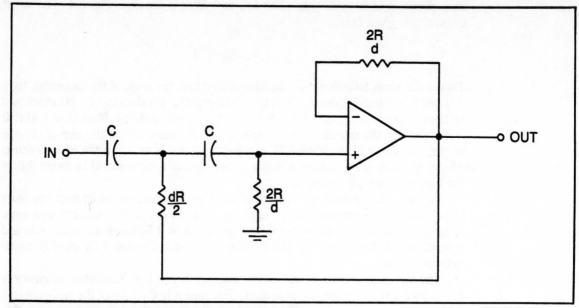

Fig. 8-5. Second-order unity-gain Sallen-Key high-pass filter.

unity. This is not usually a problem, because gain can be adjusted elsewhere in the circuit. Minimum offset is harder to attain, but this is seldom a critical factor. The equal-component-value Sallen-Key low-pass circuit is shown in Fig. 8-6, the high-pass circuit in Fig. 8-7. As with the other filters, cutoff frequency is given by:

$$f_c = 1/(2\pi RC)$$

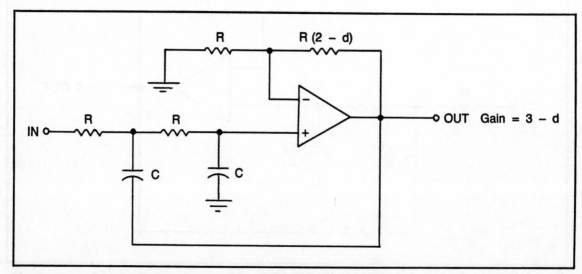

Fig. 8-6. Second-order equal-component-value Sallen-Key low-pass filter.

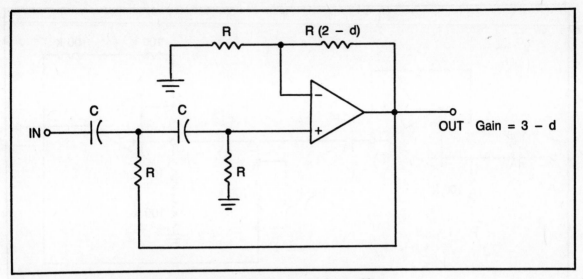

Fig. 8-7. Second-order equal-component-value Sallen-Key high-pass filter.

Damping is determined by the ratio of the feedback resistor to the inverting-input-to-ground resistor. The absolute values of these resistors are not critical, only their ratio. The gain of these circuits will be determined by the damping. For the most common second-order filter, the Butterworth maximally flat filter, damping is 1.414, and the voltage gain of these filters will be about 1.6.

Third-order filters are formed by cascading a first and a second-order filter. A fourth-order filter consists of two second-order filters, and so on. The third-order filter will be illustrated by a project.

A MODERN INFRA-SONIC FILTER

The revised RIAA standard for phono equalization calls for attenuation below 20 Hz. With a phonograph, this has several advantages. Physical movement of the stylus, as when the needle is set down on a record, no matter how gently, sends a very low frequency pulse to your speakers. If you remove the grille cloth, you will see the cones move. If the excursion caused by this impulse is too great, you can damage your speakers or amp. Even the best turntable produces some mechanical noise, or rumble, which can be reduced by a filter. Tone-arm resonances occur at about 9 Hz; there's no reason to send them though your amp to your speaker. Acoustic coupling between speakers and cartridge is most severe at infra-sonic frequencies. Even if low frequency noise doesn't damage your speakers, it will rob your amp of power. The amp will work to reproduce this infra-sonic garbage, leaving less power for music.

Figure 8-8 is a third-order infra-sonic filter. The parts list is shown in Table 8-1. Its cutoff frequency is approximately 16 Hz. This is slightly lower than most such filters, which usually are set at 18 or 20 Hz, but the component values for 16 Hz are very easy to obtain, nor is performance compromised by the slightly lower cutoff, because this filter's rolloff rate is 18 dB per octave, as compared to the 12 dB rolloff found in most

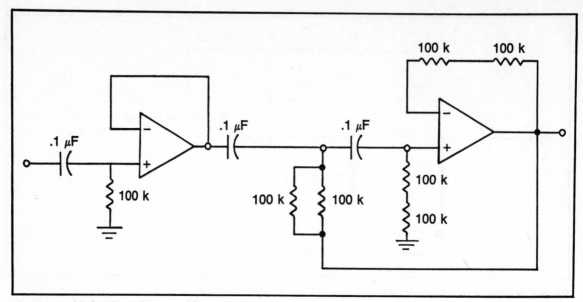

Fig. 8-8. A third-order infra-sonic filter.

such filters. The damping for the second-order stage of any maximally flat Butterworth filter is one. The parallel and series combinations of resistors shown in Fig. 8-8 implement this value. The first stage is a first-order filter set to the same frequency as the second order stage. It is possible to eliminate the extra op amp for the first-order filter by scaling this filter's impedance down by a factor of ten or more. This way it won't be affected by the second-order stage. To do this, use a one μF capacitor and a 10k resistor. The cost of a one μF plastic film capacitor is great enough, that it is probably less expensive to use the op amp.

Table 8-1. Modern Infra-Sonic Filter Parts List.

Quantity	Item
14	100 k resistors
6	0.1 μF plastic film capacitors
2	TL072 ICs
1	IC board (e.g., Radio Shack #276-159)
4	Phono plugs (optional)
—	Case, hookup wire, power supply

—AN ELECTRONIC SUBWOOFER: BASS-ENHANCING FILTER—

It's possible to improve your speakers' bass response at the same time you're filtering out infra-sonic garbage. To understand how this works requires a temporary diversion into loudspeaker design theory.

Such pioneers of speaker design theory as A. Neville Thiele and Richard H. Small demonstrated that a closed box loudspeaker behaves like a second-order filter. Its response follows the same equations as does the filter. Most closed box speakers are designed with a Q of approximately 0.9. Cascaded with a filter having a Q of 3.6, set at half the speaker's resonant frequency, the loudspeaker will produce a full octave more of clean, solid bass. Figure 8-9 shows the response of a typical loudspeaker. Figure 8-10 shows the response of the necessary filter. Figure 8-11 shows the cascaded response. The improvement will sound as obvious as it looks.

The speaker used to generate these graphs is an eight-inch driver mounted in a closed box to give a resonance frequency of 60 Hz. Its cutoff point, where the response is down three dB, occurs at approximately 55 Hz. Below 50 Hz, the bass response falls off rapidly. With the filter, the response is extended to slightly below 30 Hz. This will allow the speaker to reproduce the lowest notes on a piano at realistic levels. Bass drum and viol will sound realistic. Devotees of rock music will appreciate the ''unreal'' sound of the electric bass, just as unreal as in reality. With a larger driver, even lower response is possible.

I have measured the parameters of many speakers systems. Those that aspire to high fidelity have a Q ranging from 0.7 (most British speakers) to 1.1. The most common value is 0.9. Though I have designed for this value, the filter will perform well with any speaker in this range, indeed with any closed-box speaker you are likely to find. Only the resonance frequency of the filter will need to be adjusted to match the speaker at hand.

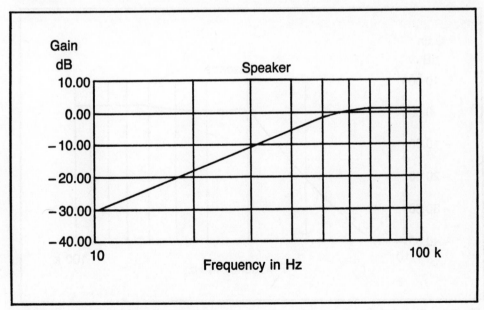

Fig. 8-9. A typical loudspeaker response curve.

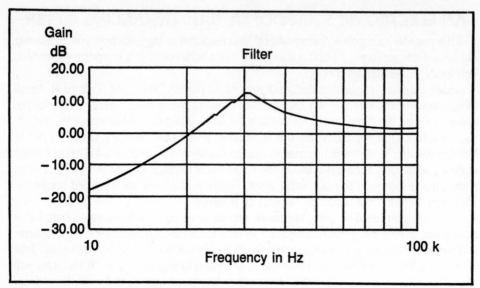

Fig. 8-10. Bass-enhancing filter response curve.

A few warnings are in order. You will need more power. If your woofer isn't designed for the extreme excursions that will be required of it, it could be damaged. And do not try this with a vented speaker system. Without the spring effect of the air in a closed box, the speaker cone is liable to fly into your lap. The extra power actually required is less than one might think, considering the peak gain the filter supplies (almost 12.5 dB). This is because the deepest bass does not provide very much of the overall program energy content. In practice, you probably have enough power with your

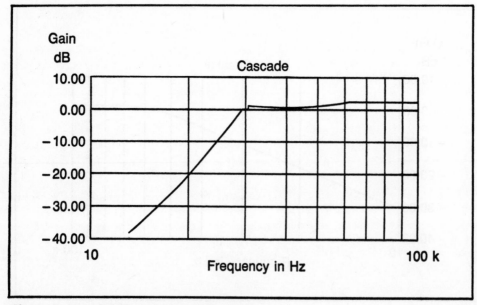

Fig. 8-11. Cascaded filter/speaker response curve.

current amp. If you have a small amp (under 30 watts), you might want to try double the power if you want to play at loud levels. I found a 30-watt amplifier supplied enough power for all but the loudest listening levels with a moderately inefficient pair of speakers when I built my first prototype.

As far as damaging the speaker goes, a little common sense will prevent that. Fuse the speaker with a two-amp fuse; you might have to add a fuse holder if your amp or speaker doesn't have one. If you hear obvious distortion, as if the speaker's suspension is bottoming out, or the popping sound of an amp clipping, then back off and listen at lower levels. For what it's worth, I have had published instructions to build similar units in *Popular Electronics* and in *Audio* magazine; I have received many letters from people telling me how pleased they were with the device, but no one has complained of speaker damage.

If your speaker is a vented box, this equalizer will not work. You might damage your speakers if you try it, and at best, it won't sound good. However, if you are designing a vented-box speaker, you can design one that is meant to be used with a filter. The filter for the vented box should have a Q of 2, or a damping factor of 0.5, which is the same thing. Details of the speaker design will be given in Chapter 10.

Figure 8-12 is the schematic for one channel of the filter. The parts list for this project is shown in Table 8-2. A second set of components will naturally be needed for the second channel. IC1 is an input buffer and level setter. Because the filter stage will introduce some gain, the input voltage divider (R1 and R2) lowers the input level by a like amount. IC2 and its associated components form a Sallen-Key equal-value components filter. R5 and R6 set the damping to 0.28. The resonant frequency of the filter is adjusted by potentiometer P1 and P2, a dual-gang unit. The component values shown allow adjustment of the filter frequency from as low as 20 Hz to as high as 60. C3 isolates the dc output from the next stage. If the unit is feeding an ac-coupled amp (one with an input capacitor) then C3 may be omitted.

The potentiometer used for P1-P2 should be a dual-gang audio- or log-taper unit. Because the higher the resistance of the pot, the lower the resonant frequency of the filter, it will be necessary to reverse-connect the pots. Otherwise, the tuning scale would be too cramped. This way, turning the pots clockwise will lower the filter frequency, and counterclockwise will raise the frequency. How to actually wire the pot is shown in Fig. 8-13. Only one of the two sets of terminals and leads is shown for simplicity, but both are connected the same way. It doesn't matter which lead goes to ground and which toward the op amp; all that matters is that the wiper be shorted to the high end of the taper. If you connect the wiper improperly, the high frequencies will be bunched together, making adjustment difficult. The leads to each pot should be formed from a twisted pair of wires to minimize noise.

You can calibrate your unit by measuring the resistance of one pot and calculating the frequency thus:

$$f = \frac{159}{0.047 \times (68 + R)}$$

where R is the measured value of the potentiometer in kilohms.

Follow the usual procedures for circuit layout and construction. Check the filter's

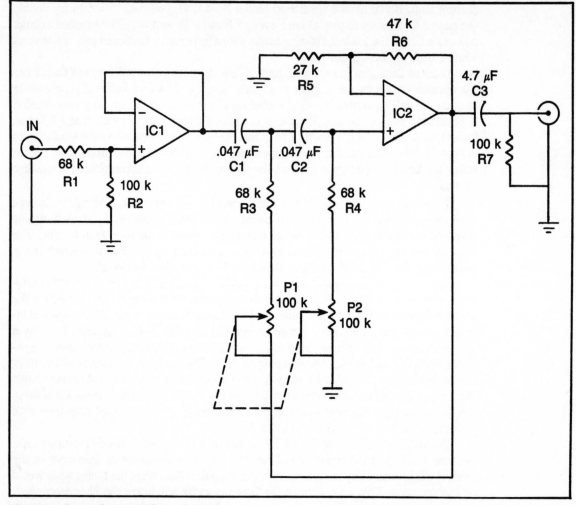

Fig. 8-12. Bass-enhancing filter schematic.

output with a scope if you have one. Otherwise, use it at a very low level until you are satisfied it is functioning properly and does not oscillate or produce other strange sounds. (I found I had to move my turntable when I tried my prototype to avoid acoustic feedback.) If you notice problems, recheck your wiring and double-check your component values. Make sure you have interpreted resistor color codes correctly.

When the circuit is debugged, you will want to set the frequency. If you know your speakers' resonant frequency, simply set the filter's frequency to one half of that value. If you have a signal generator and a VTVM or DMM, you can measure the resonance: put a 2-watt resistor, any value between 500 ohms and 1 kilohm, in series with your speaker, and feed the output of the signal generator through your amp. Measure the voltage across your speaker. It will reach a maximum at the resonance frequency.

If you are unable to make the measurement, you can approximate it. Most 8-inch speakers have a resonance of 60 Hz. Start with the filter set to 30 Hz. Larger speakers

Table 8-2. Electronic Subwoofer Bass-Enhancing Filter Parts List.

Quantity	Item
6	68 k resistors
4	100 k resistors
2	27 k resistors
2	47 k resistors
2	100 k, dual-gang, log-taper potentiometers
4	0.047 µF capacitors
2	4.7 µF (or larger) non-polarized capacitors
2	TL072 ICs
1	IC board (e.g., Radio Shack #276-159)
4	Phono plugs

are more variable, but few 10- or 12-inch speakers have a resonance lower than 45 Hz, though some are as high as 60. You will have to try varying the setting of the filter while listening. Remember, much recorded material doesn't have much bass. Most FM stations attenuate their bass below 40 Hz, as do most prerecorded cassettes and cassette decks. This leaves records and CDs. You will not hear anything from a properly adjusted filter unless deep bass is truly present. Organ music and jazz piano will come alive when the filter is properly adjusted. If you like rock music, misadjusting the filter by setting it to 50 Hz will give a pleasing bottom to rock and popular music.

Eight-inch speakers can thus reproduce all but the lowest half-octave. If the filter is used with a 10- or 12-inch speaker that has a long cone excursion, it will reproduce

Fig. 8-13. How to wire the potentiometer for the bass-enhancing filter.

accurate bass right down to 20 Hz, assuming the present low end is around 40 Hz. With adequate amplifier power, this filter will give you a truly compact subwoofer, electronically.

MULTIPLE-FEEDBACK FILTERS AND COMPUTER-AIDED DESIGN

The bandpass filter is another useful filter, but its implementation requires a multiple-feedback filter. Unlike the Sallen-Key circuit, whose implementation is straightforward, the multiple-feedback filter requires choosing four components, all of whose values interact. A computer can take most of the effort out of designing such a filter.

The bandpass filter passes only a narrow band of frequencies. The filter's Q determines just how narrow that band is. Such filters are seldom used directly in audio, but are used in side chains to detect signals, such as the multiplex carrier signal for FM reception. You can make a notch filter by subtracting the output of a bandpass filter from the main signal. I have removed 60-Hz hum from recordings this way, without removing too much of the program material. The high- and low-pass versions of the multiple-feedback filter are also useful, and unlike the Sallen-Key filters, allow for any desired combination of Q and gain. They operate in the inverting mode, which will mean better performance with some op amps. Where you want to both invert and filter a signal, the multiple-feedback configuration will do it in one step.

Figure 8-14 shows the low-pass multiple-feedback filter. The associated design formulas are:

Passband gain:

$$H_o = R_2/R_1$$

High cutoff frequency:

$$f_c = \frac{1}{2\pi} \sqrt{\frac{1}{R_2 R_3 C_1 C_2}}$$

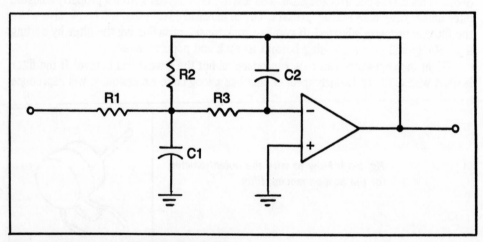

Fig. 8-14. Low-pass, multiple-feedback filter.

$$C_2 = \frac{C_1}{4Q^2 (H_0 + 1)}$$

$$R_1 = R_2/H_0$$

$$R_2 = \frac{1}{4\pi f_c Q C_2}$$

$$R_3 = \frac{1}{4\pi f_c Q C_2 (H_0 + 1)}$$

The usual procedure is to choose a likely value for C1, then calculate the values for the other components. If these values are not practical, (the resistors often come out too large or too small), then choose another value for C1 and start over. This procedure is tedious, frustrating, and error-prone, even with a scientific calculator.

Figure 8-15 shows the corresponding high-pass filter. Its design equations are:

Passband gain:

$$H_0 = C_1/C_2$$

Low cutoff frequency:

$$f_c = \frac{1}{2\pi} \sqrt{\frac{1}{R_1 R_2 C_2 C_3}}$$

$$C_2 = \frac{C_1}{H_0}$$

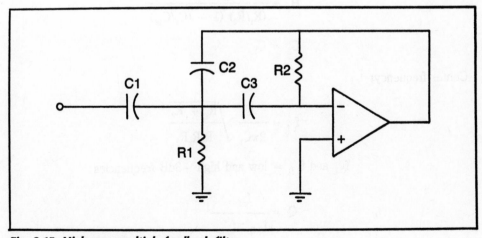

Fig. 8-15. High-pass, multiple-feedback filter.

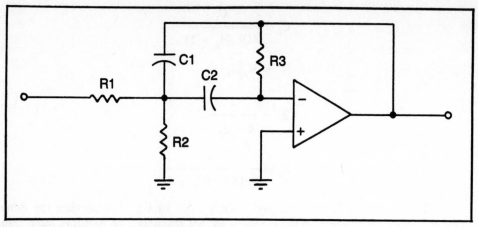

Fig. 8-16. Band-pass, multiple-feedback filter.

$$C_3 = C_1$$

$$R_1 = \frac{1}{2\pi f_c Q C_1 (2 + 1/H_0)}$$

$$R_2 = \frac{Q(2H_0 + 1)}{2\pi f_c C_1}$$

The design procedure is similar to the low-pass filter, and just as tedious. Figure 8-16 is the band-pass filter. Its design equations are:

Passband gain:

$$H_0 = \frac{1}{(R_1/R_3)(1 + (C_1/C_2))}$$

$$C_2 = C_1$$

Center frequency: f_{cf}

$$f_{cf} = \frac{1}{2\pi C_1} \sqrt{\frac{R_1 + R_2}{R_1 R_2 R_3}}$$

f_{CL} and f_{CH} = low and high −3dB frequencies

$$Q = \frac{f_{cf}}{f_{CH} - f_{CL}}$$

$$R_1 = \frac{Q}{H_0 2 - \pi f_{C\,F} C_1}$$

$$R_2 = \frac{Q}{(2Q^2 - H_0) 2\,\pi f_{C\,F} C_1}$$

$$R_3 = \frac{Q}{C_1 \pi f_{C\,F}}$$

Again, you start the procedure by choosing an arbitrary value for C1; all else follows, given the desired Q and center frequency. If you are lucky enough to get it on the first try, you will have a working filter after a good many minutes of calculation. If you are not lucky, it will take many hours.

If you have examined the above equations, you will notice a relationship between Q and the −3 dB points of the bandpass filter. Knowing the range of frequencies that must be passed enables you to choose the proper Q for a filter that will do the job. But if the passband is too wide, you will have to cascade a high-pass and a low-pass filter to meet the requirement.

The programs in Figs. 8-17 through 8-20 were originally written in BASIC for the Apple II+, and will run as written on any machine in that family. Translation to other BASIC dialects should be very straightforward. The programs are available on disk (see the Appendix for details).

The first program (Fig. 8-17) will design either high- or low-pass filters. The second (Fig. 8-19) is for band-pass filters. You will need to refer to Figs. 8-14 through 8-16 for component placement. The programs' operation should be self-explanatory. If you follow the sample run in Fig. 8-18 for the high-pass/low-pass program, you will see the design of a pair of filters, one high-pass, one low, with cutoff frequencies of 2500 Hz. These filters have a Q of one for use in a third-order Butterworth network. They could be used for an active speaker crossover.

```
]LOAD MULTIPLE FEEDBACK HPLP
]LIST

10    HOME : REM    CLEAR SCREEN

20    PRINT "MULTIPLE FEEDBACK FIL
      TER"
30    PRINT "DESIGN ROUTINE"
40    PRINT
50    PRINT "BY RICHARD KAUFMAN"
60    PRINT : PRINT "HIGHPASS(H),
```

Fig. 8-17. High-pass/low-pass multiple-feedback filter program.

```
        LOWPASS(L), OR BOTH(B)": INPUT
        RSP$: PRINT
70      PRINT "WHAT IS THE FILTER FR
        EQUENCY"
80      PRINT "     IN HERTZ"
90      INPUT "     ?";FC
100     PRINT
110     Q = .707
120     INPUT "IS THE Q = .707? (Y
        OR N)";Q$
130     IF Q$ = "Y" THEN 160
140     PRINT
150     INPUT "WHAT IS THE VALUE OF
        Q? ";Q
160     PRINT : PRINT "WHAT IS THE
        DESIRED GAIN"
170     PRINT "     (VOLTAGE RATIO,
        NOT DECIBELS)"
180     INPUT "     ?";HO: PRINT
190     PRINT "THE CAPACITOR VALUE
        FOR C1 IS IN"
200     PRINT "     PICOFARADS (P)"
        .
210     PRINT "     MICROFARADS (M)
        "
220     INPUT "     ?";C$
230     IF C$ <  > "P" AND C$ <  >
        "M" GOTO 190
240     IF C$ = "P" THEN CF = 1E -
        12:
250     IF C$ = "M" THEN CF = 1E -
        6
260     PRINT : INPUT "WHAT IS THE
        VALUE OF C1?";C1
270     C2 = (C1 * CF) / (4 * Q ^ 2 *
        (HO + 1))
280     R2 = 1 / (4 * 3.1416 * FC *
        Q * C2)
290     R1 = R2 / HO
300     R3 = 1 / (4 * 3.1416 * FC *
        Q * C2 * (HO + 1))
310     IF RSP$ = "H" THEN  GOTO 40
        0
320     PRINT : PRINT "LOW PASS VAL
        UES:": PRINT
330     PRINT "C2="C2 / CF;" ";C$;"
        FD"
340     PRINT "R1=" INT (R1);" OHMS
```

```
350   PRINT "R2=" INT (R2);" OHMS
      "
360   PRINT "R3=" INT (R3);" OHMS
      "
370   PRINT : INPUT "ARE THESE VA
      LUES OK? (Y OR N) ";ANS$: PRINT

380   IF ANS$ = "N" THEN 190
390   IF RSP$ = "L" THEN 510
400  C3 = C1:C2 = C1 / HO
410  R1 = 1 / (2 * 3.1416 * FC *
     Q * C1 * CF * (2 + 1 / HO))
420  R2 = (Q * (2 * HO + 1)) / (2
     * 3.1416 * FC * C1 * CF)
430   PRINT
440   PRINT "HIGH PASS VALUES": PRINT

450   PRINT "C2=";C2;" ";C$;"FD"
460   PRINT "C3=";C3;" ";C$;"FD"
470   PRINT "R1=" INT (R1);" OHMS
      "
480   PRINT "R2=" INT (R2);" OHMS
      "
490   PRINT : INPUT "ARE THESE VA
      LUES OK? (Y OR N) ";ANS$: PRINT

500   IF ANS$ = "N" THEN 190
510   INPUT "WOULD YOU LIKE TO DE
      SIGN ANOTHER FILTER? ";ANS$
520   IF ANS$ = "Y" THEN 10
530   PRINT : PRINT "BYE!"
540   PRINT  CHR$ (4)"RUN HELLO"
```

```
]RUN
MULTIPLE FEEDBACK FILTER
DESIGN ROUTINE

BY RICHARD KAUFMAN

HIGHPASS(H), LOWPASS(L), OR BOTH(B)
?H

WHAT IS THE FILTER FREQUENCY
```

Fig. 8-18. High-pass/low-pass program sample run.

```
        IN HERTZ
        ?2500

    IS THE Q = .707? (Y OR N)N

    WHAT IS THE VALUE OF Q? 1

    WHAT IS THE DESIRED GAIN
        (VOLTAGE RATIO, NOT DECIBELS)
        ?1

    THE CAPACITOR VALUE FOR C1 IS IN
        PICOFARADS (P)
        MICROFARADS (M)
        ?P

    WHAT IS THE VALUE OF C1?1000

    HIGH PASS VALUES

    C2=1000 PFD
    C3=1000 PFD
    R1=21220 OHMS
    R2=190985 OHMS

    ARE THESE VALUES OK? (Y OR N) N

    THE CAPACITOR VALUE FOR C1 IS IN
        PICOFARADS (P)
        MICROFARADS (M)
        ?P

    WHAT IS THE VALUE OF C1?1800

    HIGH PASS VALUES

    C2=1800 PFD
    C3=1800 PFD
    R1=11789 OHMS
    R2=106103 OHMS

    ARE THESE VALUES OK? (Y OR N) Y

    WOULD YOU LIKE TO DESIGN ANOTHER FILTER? Y
    MULTIPLE FEEDBACK FILTER
    DESIGN ROUTINE

    BY RICHARD KAUFMAN
```

```
HIGHPASS(H), LOWPASS(L), OR BOTH(B)
?L
WHAT IS THE FILTER FREQUENCY
      IN HERTZ
      ?2500

IS THE Q = .707? (Y OR N)N

WHAT IS THE VALUE OF Q? 1

WHAT IS THE DESIRED GAIN
      (VOLTAGE RATIO, NOT DECIBELS)
      ?1
THE CAPACITOR VALUE FOR C1 IS IN
      PICOFARADS (P)
      MICROFARADS (M)
      ?P

WHAT IS THE VALUE OF C1?1800

LOW PASS VALUES:

C2=225 PFD
R1=141470 OHMS
R2=141470 OHMS
R3=70735 OHMS

ARE THESE VALUES OK? (Y OR N) N

THE CAPACITOR VALUE FOR C1 IS IN
      PICOFARADS (P)
      MICROFARADS (M)
      ?P

WHAT IS THE VALUE OF C1?4700

LOW PASS VALUES:

C2=587.5 PFD
R1=54180 OHMS
R2=54180 OHMS
R3=27090 OHMS

ARE THESE VALUES OK? (Y OR N) Y

WOULD YOU LIKE TO DESIGN ANOTHER FILTER? N

BYE!
```

```
]LOAD BANDPASS
]LIST

  10  HOME : REM   CLEAR SCREEN

  20  PRINT "MULTIPLE FEEDBACK FIL
      TER"
  25  PRINT "BANDPASS"
  30  PRINT "DESIGN ROUTINE"
  40  PRINT
  50  PRINT "BY RICHARD KAUFMAN"
  70  PRINT "WHAT IS THE FILTER FR
      EQUENCY"
  80  PRINT "      IN HERTZ"
  90  INPUT "      ?";FC
  100  PRINT
  140  PRINT
  150  INPUT "WHAT IS THE VALUE OF
       Q? ";Q
  160  PRINT : PRINT "WHAT IS THE
       DESIRED GAIN"
  170  PRINT "      (VOLTAGE RATIO,
       NOT DECIBELS)
  180  INPUT "      ?";HO: PRINT
  190  PRINT "THE CAPACITOR VALUE
       FOR C1 IS IN"
  200  PRINT "      PICOFARADS (P)"

  210  PRINT "      MICROFARADS (M)
      "
  220  INPUT "      ?";C$
  230  IF C$ <  > "P" AND C$ <  >
       "M" GOTO 190
  240  IF C$ = "P" THEN CF = 1E -
       12:
  250  IF C$ = "M" THEN CF = 1E -
       6
  260  PRINT : INPUT "WHAT IS THE
       VALUE OF C1?";C1
  270 R1 = Q / (HO * 2 * 3.1416 *
       C1 * CF * FC)
  280 R2 = Q / ((2 * Q ^ 2 - HO) *
       2 * 3.1416 * FC * C1 * CF)
  290 R3 = Q / (C1 * CF * 3.1416 *
       FC)
```

Fig. 8-19. Bandpass multiple-feedback program.

```
320   PRINT : PRINT "BANDPASS VAL
      UES:": PRINT
340   PRINT "R1=" INT (R1);" OHMS
      "
350   PRINT "R2=" INT (R2);" OHMS
      "
360   PRINT "R3=" INT (R3);" OHMS
      "
370   PRINT : INPUT "ARE THESE VA
      LUES OK? (Y OR N) ";ANS$: PRINT

380   IF ANS$ = "N" THEN 190
510   INPUT "WOULD YOU LIKE TO DE

      SIGN ANOTHER FILTER? ";ANS$
520   IF ANS$ = "Y" THEN 10
530   PRINT : PRINT "BYE!"
540   REM  PRINT CHR$ (4)"RUN HEL
      LO"
```

```
]P
]RUN
MULTIPLE FEEDBACK FILTER
BANDPASS
DESIGN ROUTINE

BY RICHARD KAUFMAN
WHAT IS THE FILTER FREQUENCY
        IN HERTZ
        ?3938


WHAT IS THE VALUE OF Q? 12.5

WHAT IS THE DESIRED GAIN
        (VOLTAGE RATIO, NOT DECIBELS)
        ?1

THE CAPACITOR VALUE FOR C1 IS IN
        PICOFARADS (P)
        MICROFARADS (M)
        ?P

WHAT IS THE VALUE OF C1?1000
```

Fig. 8-20. Bandpass program sample run.

```
BANDPASS VALUES:

R1=505188 OHMS
R2=1621 OHMS
R3=1010376 OHMS

ARE THESE VALUES OK? (Y OR N) N

THE CAPACITOR VALUE FOR C1 IS IN
     PICOFARADS (P)
     MICROFARADS (M)
     ?P

WHAT IS THE VALUE OF C1?4700

BANDPASS VALUES:

R1=107486 OHMS
R2=345 OHMS
R3=214973 OHMS

ARE THESE VALUES OK? (Y OR N) Y

WOULD YOU LIKE TO DESIGN ANOTHER FILTER? N

BYE!
```

The sample run for the bandpass program (Fig. 8-20) is for a filter with a center frequency of 3938 Hz and a Q of 12.5. Such a filter could be used to look for signals, or an absence of signals, in this narrow frequency range. A more practical use of a bandpass filter might be to design a high-Q filter centered at 60 Hz, then subtract its output from the main signal. You can remove hum from recordings this way, without degrading the sound too much.

REFERENCES

Jung, Walter G. *IC Op-Amp Cookbook*. Indianapolis, IN: Howard W. Sams & Co., Inc.,1974

Lancaster, Don. *Active Filter Cookbook*. Indianapolis, IN: Howard W. Sams & Co., Inc., 1975

9
Active Crossover Networks

CROSSOVER NETWORKS ARE SPECIALIZED FILTERS, BUT THEIR REQUIREMENTS ARE unique, and tricky enough to warrant a separate chapter. Using active filters with two amplifiers (biamplification) for speaker crossovers has many advantages over the use of passive filters. One can attain a level of performance just not possible with passive circuits; active filter configurations can be extremely difficult, and sometimes impossible, to implement with passive devices. Much sharper rates of rolloff are feasible with an active filter. This makes it possible to use tweeters at lower frequencies than in a passive system. (The tweeter is not called upon to deliver as much power at lower frequencies, and may thus be cut in lower.) Performance of active crossovers is predictable; passive components interact with driver voice coils in ways that can produce audible peaks outside a driver's range. The main drawback of an active crossover—an extra amplifier for each driver—is also an advantage. Biamplification lessens the possibility of intermodulate distortion between low and high-frequency signals. This might account for the frequent subjective impression of cleaner sound with a bi-amped system. Then a pair of medium-power amps might be less expensive than one high-power amp, yet give the same apparent sound level in a bi-amped system.

First and second-order filters are the kind most commonly found in passive speaker crossover networks. The first-order network has a disadvantage in that its rate of attenuation is so slow that both drivers must tolerate signals well outside their intended range. Finding or designing drivers with such broad spectrum response is difficult, especially for tweeters, which tend to burn out when called on to deliver more than a few watts, particularly below two or three kHz. Such simple networks do have some advantages. One that is shared by all odd-order networks is that the high and low outputs are 90 degrees out of phase. This results in the delivery of both constant voltage and constant power throughout the crossover region. Another advantage is that the first-order network is allpass, that is, the outputs sum to be identical to the inputs. But the advantages of first-order crossovers are outweighed by the problems caused by their low rate of attenuation, which are not limited to power-handling problems. If two drivers are separated by a significant portion of a wavelength, they will interfere with each other over the range of frequencies where their outputs overlap. This effect is very severe for first-order networks, with their slow rates of attenuation. The result is this: because drivers are usually mounted one atop another, vertical dispersion is irregular, and varies with frequency. Most commonly, there is a lobe of increased response at the crossover frequency, directed downward. The angle of this lobe changes with frequency, and depends on the distance between the centers of the two drivers. This is audible as a coloration of the sound that varies with listening position. A coaxial driver, with the woofer and tweeter voice coils forming concentric cylinders, would eliminate these interference effects. As far as I know, Tannoy is the only company which makes such a speaker system.

A second-order Butterworth crossover avoids the interference problem if certain conditions are met. Because such a crossover's outputs are 180 degrees out of phase, they cancel. The result is a null at the crossover frequency. This is not good. That is why the higher frequency driver's leads are reversed, so its output will be inverted. Now the tweeter will be in phase with the woofer at the crossover point, though its signal will be inverted throughout most of its range. Now the phase relationships between the drivers is such that the lobe caused by their mutual interference is symmetrical and directed in a horizontal direction toward the listener. The Butterworth crossover with inverted tweeter will have a response irregularity. When the filter outputs are summed, there is a voltage gain of about three decibels at the crossover frequency. Although this filter's outputs don't voltage-sum to unity, they do power-sum to unity. This means that in a diffuse sound environment, such as a reflective listening room, the three-dB bump won't be too objectionable.

THIRD-ORDER CROSSOVERS

Third-order passive networks are seldom found in speakers. Their successful use depends on careful design, matching capacitor and inductor values to the drivers with a high degree of precision, and compensating for any frequency-dependent irregularities in the drivers. Very strict tolerances must be maintained, both in the components' values, and in the manufacturing process of the drivers. Such control is just not available to the amateur, but an active network with just as tight a tolerance is easy to build.

The third-order Butterworth filter consists of a first-order filter at the desired frequency, followed by a second-order filter with a damping factor of one set to the same frequency. The infrasonic filter in the previous chapter was third-order. Two such filters, one high-pass and one low, will make a third-order Butterworth crossover network. The outputs of the two filters will be 270 degrees out of phase. Inverting the higher frequency driver will put the two outputs 90 degrees out of phase. This inversion is generally thought to be desirable because it reduces *group delay*—the rate at which the phase changes. Group delay distortion does seem to be audible on certain kinds of signals, particularly at low frequencies, though it is much less significant than linear frequency response in determining a speaker's quality.

The interference effect between drivers used with a third-order crossover will also cause lobes in the system's vertical response that are asymmetrical on axis to the listener. Simply translated, this means the system will sound different if you sit on the floor, on a chair, or stand up, and this change will be different at different frequencies. The speaker's response won't be flat in any direction. If the crossover is used for a subwoofer below 150 Hz, the drivers can be close enough together so that the lobing will not occur. The third-order network is a valid option when a sharp cutoff is required of both drivers in a subwoofer system.

Even though a third-order crossover's outputs voltage-sum to unity, the output is still not considered allpass. The reason is that some portion of the original signal is lost. This can be seen by studying the transfer functions that describe a filter's responses. For a second-order filter, the response-defining equations are:

$$\text{Low-Pass Output} = \frac{1}{S^2 + dS + 1}$$

$$\text{High-Pass Output} = \frac{S^2}{S^2 + dS + 1}$$

where:

d = Damping Factor (V_2 for a Butterworth Filter)
S = Complex Frequency Factor = $2\pi fV - 1$

Examining these two equations, it is obvious that the term "dS" will be missing from the numerator when the high and low-pass outputs are summed. The situation is similar for the third-order crossover, except that there are two missing terms, "d_1S^2" and "d_2S." By supplying the missing term(s), it's possible to construct an allpass crossover.

——SECOND-ORDER ASYMMETRIC ALLPASS CROSSOVER——

Allpass crossovers are difficult to realize with passive networks, but it can be done by using an extra driver to supply the missing dS term. (Phillips once marketed such a speaker.) Active circuitry allows you to do the job much more easily. Figure 9-1 is the circuit for a second-order allpass crossover, and the parts list is shown in Table 9-1. IC3 forms a second-order Butterworth filter, with a resonant frequency of approximately 110 Hz. Thus, the low-pass response will be second-order and maximally flat. IC1 and IC2 effectively subtract the output of the filter from the main signal. Clearly, the summed response from the two drivers should be equal to the input signal. All the components of the original signal are passed.

In fact, this crossover will suffer from the same problem of interference between drivers that plagues the odd-order crossovers. This is why it is recommended only for subwoofer crossovers, below 160 Hz. At these frequencies, the drivers will be acousti-

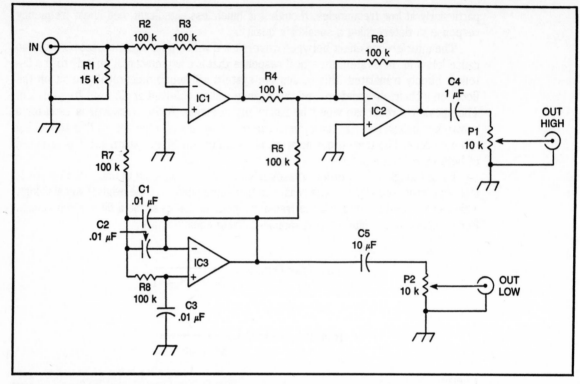

Fig. 9-1. Asymmetric crossover for 112 Hz.

cally close together, because the wavelength of the crossover frequency is so large. At 100 Hz, half a wavelength is 5.5 feet. If the speakers' centers are closer than half a wavelength, interference won't be a problem. Under these conditions, the fact that the crossover is allpass results in a seamless transition between the subwoofer and the rest of the system. Of the crossovers I have tried, I am most pleased with this one for subwoofer applications.

The derived high-pass response does have some peculiarities. Rolloff is only six dB per octave, no matter what rolloff rate of the filter used. That is why the crossover is configured so that the derived response is high-pass rather than low-pass. Otherwise, the subwoofer's response would extend too high, causing interference effects and response irregularities. Also, if you want to sum the low-pass outputs of both channels, in order to use a single subwoofer, the highs in the subwoofer would interfere with the stereo effect.

Figure 9-2 shows the response of the low-pass filter and the derived high-pass response. You can easily see why the crossover is called "asymmetric." There is a two-dB bump in the high-pass response at the crossover frequency. The bump extends up to 300 Hz, and the response is attenuated much more gradually than the low-pass response. Your main speakers will have to have decent bass response in order to work with this filter. Mini-satellites are out. Main speakers with a response down to one-half the crossover frequency or lower are recommended.

Using a higher-order filter in this configuration will not help the high-pass rolloff.

108

Table 9-1. Asymmetric All-pass Crossover Parts List.

Parts list is for one channel only.

Resistors

R1	15 k
R2,R3,R4,R5,R6,R7,R8	100 k, 1%

Pontentiometers

P1,P2	10 k, dual-gang, log-taper (half used in each channel)

Capacitors

C1,C2,C3	0.01 μF plastic film
C4	1 μF nonpolarized
C5	10 μF nonpolarized

Op Amps

IC1,IC2,IC3	One-half of TL072; three chips required for two channels

Miscellaneous

IC board (e.g., Radio Shack #276-154)
Four phono plugs, case, hookup wire, power supply

It will always be six dB per octave. But beware! The bump will grow larger (but narrower in bandwidth) as filter order increases, making exorbitant demands on the high-pass driver. For a third-order filter, the bump will be over four dB.

The resistors used in conjunction with IC1 and IC2 are not critical in value, but they must be closely matched. This means one percent tolerance. One-hundred kilohm resistors are shown here and should be readily obtainable. R1 provides a ground path for the bias current of IC3. Without it, the circuit won't work. The capacitors that form the filter, (C1, C2 and C3) are not critical as to accuracy. Five percent tolerance is adequate, as it is for all other components. The output capacitors block offset voltages and may be omitted if successive stages have input capacitors. If used, they must be nonpolarized. Plastic film ones work best. If you cannot find a plastic film, 10-μF cap for the low-pass output, bypass an electrolytic with a 1-μF film capacitor. The output

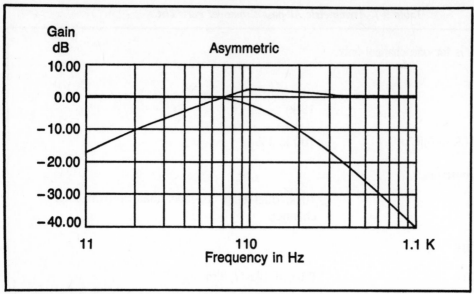

Gain
dB

Asymmetric

Fig. 9-2. *Second-order asymmetric crossover response.*

potentiometers are for adjusting the relative levels of the lows and highs. You may use linear, PC-mounting, screwdriver-adjustable pots if you are seldom going to change speakers or amps. Otherwise, log or audio taper pots that you can adjust without opening the case are convenient.

It is possible to combine the bass-enhancing filter of Chapter 8 with this crossover on one PC board. The bass-filter should follow the crossover to avoid any possible degradation to the high-pass signal.

————FOURTH-ORDER LINKWITZ-RILEY CROSSOVER————

The Linkwitz-Riley crossover will keep both outputs in phase at the crossover point without the bump in frequency response that characterizes the even-order Butterworth crossovers. This class of crossover will voltage-sum to unity throughout the crossover region. Unlike the asymmetric crossover, the response is not all-pass; there are phase changes throughout the crossover region. The audibility of such phase changes is controversial. Non-linear phase shift seems to be less audible at high frequencies than at low, but there is no solid evidence that the amount present in a Linkwitz crossover will be audible at any frequency. This is probably the crossover of choice for any frequency above 150 Hz and is superior in many respects to the asymmetric crossover at lower frequencies.

The second-order Linkwitz filter consists of a high and a low-pass filter, both with a resonant frequency set to the crossover point, and a damping factor equal to two. The high pass output needs to be inverted to prevent cancellation at the crossover frequency. Such filters are easy to implement passively in loudspeakers and are becoming increasingly popular. The performance of the fourth-order Linkwitz crossover is so superior that there seems to be little point in building a second-order active version. (There are no odd-order Linkwitz crossovers.) Some English speaker manufacturers use passive fourth-order Linkwitz-Riley filters. This requires sophisticated computer-aided design and measurement in the manufacturing process, because driver characteristics greatly alter component values and network configuration from theoretical values.

The fourth-order Linkwitz high- and low-pass sections both consist of two cascaded Butterworth filters, each set to the desired crossover point. The schematic in Fig. 9-3 shows one channel of such a filter, with a crossover point of 3000 Hz. The parts list is shown in Table 9-2. These are the unity-gain, Sallen-Key filters covered in Chapter 8. Don't let the different circuit topology mislead you. The design information in Chapter 8 should permit you to determine the necessary component values to set the frequency to any desired value. You may also scale the component values given in Fig. 9-3: Increase the resistor values for all resistors except R1 and P1 by the factor you wish to decrease the frequency, or decrease the resistor values by the factor you wish to increase the frequency. Alternately, you may scale the capacitors the same way, or even a combination scaling of both types of components. For example, suppose you wanted a 2000-Hz crossover. This is ⅔ of 3 kHz. Multiply the resistor values by ¾. R2, R3,

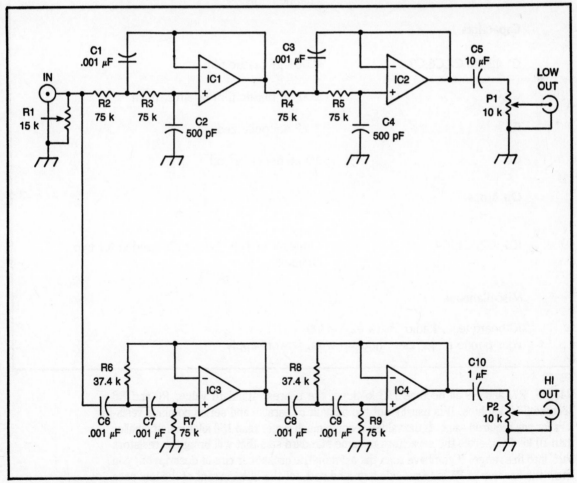

Fig. 9-3. Linkwitz-Riley crossover for 3000 Hz.

Table 9-2. Linkwitz-Riley Crossover Parts List.

Part list is for one channel only.

Resistors

R1	15 k
R2,R3,R4,R5,R7,R9	75 k
R6,R8	37.4 k

Potentiometers

P1,P2	10 k, dual-gang, log-taper (half used in each channel)

Capacitors

C1,C3,C6,C7,C8,C9	0.001 μF plastic film
C2,C4	500 pF plastic film or silver mica
C5	1 μF nonpolarized
C6	10 μF nonpolarized

Op Amps

IC1,IC2,IC3,IC4	One-half of TL072; four ICs needed for two channels

Miscellaneous

IC board (e.g., Radio Shack #276-154)
Four phono plugs, case, hookup wire, power supply

R4, R5, R7, and R9 all become 113 kilohms, the nearest standard value. R6 and R8 become 56.2 kilohms. It is usually not too difficult to parallel and series combine resistors for any required value. If the values become much larger than 150 kilohms, or smaller than 10 kilohms, scale the capacitors to some standard size that will bring the resistors back into this range. If you have read the asymmetric crossover circuit description, you know the function of R1 is to provide a ground path for the bias current of the low-pass filter's op amps. The output capacitors and potentiometers serve the same function as in the asymmetric crossover, and the same comments apply.

Figure 9-4 shows the frequency response of the two legs of this crossover. Comparing this response to that in Fig. 9-2, it is evident that the attenuation rate is much greater for this filter. The region of driver overlap is limited to a half octave on either side of the crossover frequency, and the interference between drivers will be symmetrical with respect to the listener. (This assumes they are mounted with their voice coils in the same vertical plane.) Because the cutoff is so sharp, neither driver handles significant amounts of out-of-band information. This helps protect the tweeter from overload. In fact, the usable frequency range of many tweeters is extended downward because of this. Many woofers have gross response irregularities in their upper frequency ranges. With a conventional second-order network, peaks well above the crossover point are sometimes clearly—and painfully—audible. This crossover hides such faults in the basement of its response curve.

You might think the fourth-order Linkwitz-Riley circuit to be the ultimate crossover, it isn't because this chapter isn't over yet. If there were some reasonable way to get even sharper rates of attenuation, the region of mutual driver interaction over the octave centered about the crossover frequency could be made so narrow as to eliminate driver interference as a factor in the speaker design.

A 100-DB PER OCTAVE CROSSOVER

I pointed out in this chapter's introductory section that summing the outputs of second-order high- and low-pass filters results in a null at the crossover frequency. Rather than adding all of the high-pass signal to the low-pass, if you add just some fraction thereof, the null can be moved up or down in frequency. The high-pass response of this low-pass filter will bounce back up at frequencies higher than the null, but if it is cascaded with another filter, this unwanted response can be further attenuated. There is a whole class

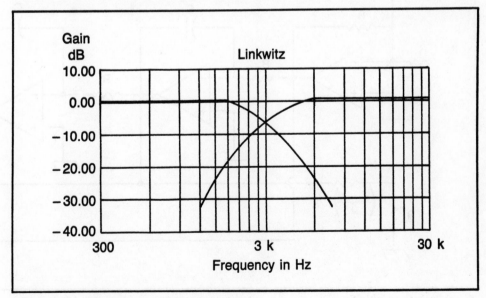

Fig. 9-4. Linkwitz-Riley crossover response.

of such filters, called *elliptical* or *Cauer filters.* The crossover described here does not use elliptical filters as properly defined, but it is similar. The actual values used for the damping of the various stages, and the summed ratio of high-pass to low-pass, were derived experimentally using a computer. The goal was a voltage-summing response with very steep attenuation.

To understand how the circuit works, it is necessary to consider yet another kind of filter circuit. The state variable filter is shown in Fig. 9-5. This circuit is more complex than the single op amp circuits used so far, but it also provides three outputs: high-, low-, and bandpass. Also, all the responses have the same resonant frequency and Q, because their parameters are determined by the same components. Like the multiple-feedback filter, this one inverts the high- and low-pass outputs, but it does not invert the bandpass response.

The resistors labeled rf and the capacitors labeled C determine the resonant frequency according to the formula:

$$f_R = \frac{1}{2\pi RC}$$

The value of the resistors labeled "R" is not critical, but they must match. Damping is determined by the resistor labeled "R_d," and by the bandpass feedback resistor, which must equal $R_d(3-d)/d$. This filter uses one more op amp than the Sallen-Key circuits. It is used here only because the high- and low-pass responses should be exactly complementary in order to derive the desired null just outside the pass band.

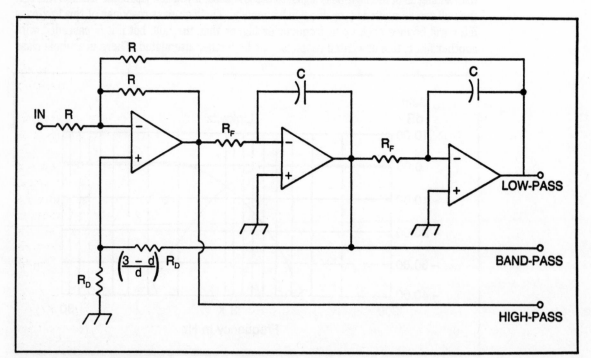

Fig. 9-5. State-variable filter.

114

Figure 9-6 is the schematic of the 100-dB-per-octave crossover, and Table 9-3 gives the parts list. IC2 through IC4 form a state-variable filter. IC5 and IC6 are inverting summers; they set the notches in the low- and high-pass responses at 2100 Hz and 4500 Hz. They also restore correct absolute polarity to the signals. R8 and R9 limit the low frequency gain of the op amps, so they won't saturate. IC7 and IC8 form third-order filters. The passive first-order filters that precede the active second-order stages must have an impedance level one-tenth that of the active filter components. Note that the Sallen-Key filters have about 2.5 dB gain. The high-pass output is capacitively coupled, and its level is set by P2. The same comments apply here as in the output potentiometers and capacitors of the Linkwitz crossover. The low-pass output's level is set by P1. Unlike the other circuits described earlier, the output is dc coupled (i.e., there is no capacitor). This is possible because of the network feeding IC1. (You may omit this network if you wish, but if you do, use a capacitor after IC7.)

Because op amps are available two and four to an IC, there was an extra one left over, making it possible to incorporate an offset adjustment circuit. R30 and R29 are connected to the positive and negative supply rails to form a voltage divider. P3 divides the 1.4-volt drop across the pair of diodes, D1 ad D2. C10 filters out the diode noise. The voltage taken from the wiper of P3 is mixed with the input signal, so any dc offset introduced into the circuit can be nulled. You will need to measure the no-signal voltage level at the output of IC7, adjusting P3 to get it as low as possible. The setting of P3 will be temperature sensitive, so let the circuit warm up for half an hour before making a final adjustment. For testing, the approximate adjustment made when the circuit is first powered up might be adequate. Note that if the preamp feeding this circuit is not ac coupled or otherwise designed to eliminate dc offset voltage, an input coupling capacitor of approximately 4.7 μF should be used. Most preamps are so equipped, and the capacitor will seldom be necessary. If in doubt, measure the preamp's offset voltage. If it is only one or two milliamps, forget the capacitor.

Frequency can be adjusted by scaling the frequency-determining components, which are described as such in the parts list in the Appendix. The frequency-scaling procedure is the same described for the Linkwitz filter.

This circuit is much more complicated than any other in the book, and I don't recommend it as a first project. Even more than the other circuits, careful layout of the components is necessary before soldering begins.

Figure 9-7 is a graph of the low-pass filter's response. Compared to the Linkwitz crossover, response falls off much more rapidly outside the passband, and though it rises again, it is never less than 26 dB below the passband response. Figure 9-8 shows the combined response of the low- and high-pass legs of the crossover. The slight sag in the middle is not significant, being less than half a decibel. Which filter is better, the 100-dB per octave one or the Linkwitz-Riley? The Linkwitz filter does not have such sharp attenuation, so the drivers must deliver more out-of-band energy. The 100-dB filter will have the asymmetric interference effect in the crossover region due to its being odd-order, but the crossover region is less than one-third octave, so this should not be significant. The Linkwitz filter is better damped, but the ringing of the 100-dB filter (of any filter) will not be audible if it dies out faster than the listening room's reverberation time. There will be no risk of this in a home listening room if the 100-dB crossover is

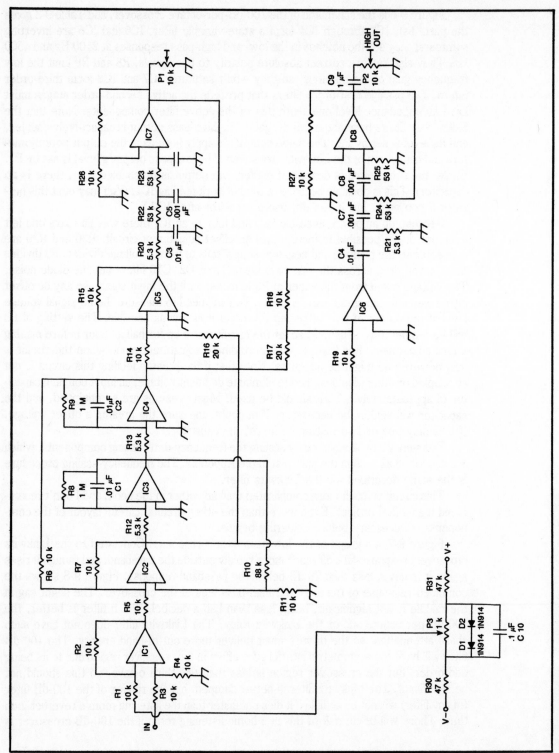

Fig. 9-6. 100-dB per octave crossover at 3000 Hz.

Table 9-3. 100-dB per Octave Parts List.

Part list is for one channel only.

Resistors

R1,R2,R3,R4,R5,R6,R7,R11,R14	10 kilohms
R15,R18,R19,R26,R27	
R8,R9	1 megohm
R10	88 k (determines Q)
R12,R13,R20,R21	5.3 k (determine Frequency)
R16,R17	20 k (or use two 10 k in series)
R22,R23,R24,R25	53 k (determine frequency)
R28,R29	3.77 k (determine Q)
R30,R31	47 k

Potentiometers

P1,P2	10 k, dual-gang, log-taper (half used in each channel)
P3	1 k, PC mounting

Capacitors

C1,C2,C3,C4	0.01 μF plastic film (determine frequency)
C5,C6,C7,C8	0.001 μF plastic film (determine frequency)
C9	1 μF nonpolarized
C10	0.1 μF plastic film

Diodes

D1,D2	1N914 or 1N4148

Op Amps

IC1 through IC8   Two TL074 or four TL072 or equivalent

Miscellaneous

IC board (e.g., Radio Shack #276-154)
Four phono plugs, case, hookup wire, power supply

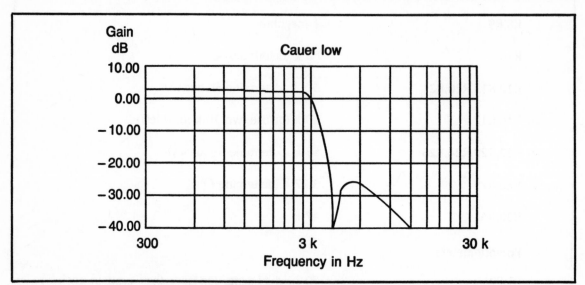

Fig. 9-7. Low-pass filter response for 100-dB per octave crossover.

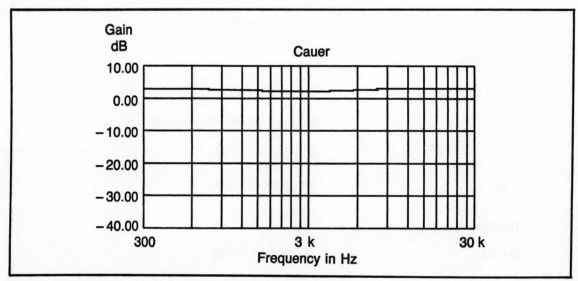

Fig. 9-8. Voltage-summed response for 100-dB per octave crossover.

restricted to frequencies above 200 Hz. The Linkwitz filter uses fewer parts and half as many op amps, so it is considerably easier to build. Direct listening comparisons have not been performed, so it is not possible to say which sounds better.

There are loudspeakers which have similar passive crossovers. JSE manufactures such a loudspeaker; they won't say how the crossover works, beyond smiling and muttering something about "zero-pole cancellation." Because that is essentially how an elliptical filter works, one suspects they have designed a similar passive filter. This is an impressive feat, for such a circuit would be even more sensitive to driver parameters than a normal crossover. The sound of these speakers is truly wonderful; there is no change in timbre with vertical angle. Try standing up as you listen to a more conventional speaker and you will notice an unpleasant change.

DIGITAL FILTERS

The perfect crossover would consist of ideal filters whose response is ruler-flat in the passband but drops to zero at the crossover point. Such perfect filters can't be made with purely analog techniques, though the design of the 100-dB crossover was an attempt to come closer to this ideal. All analog filters show considerable phase shift at their resonant frequency. When this phase shift is linear, the attenuation rate of the filter suffers. When it is not linear, group delay distortion is present. The FIR (finite impulse response) or non-recursive class of digital filter can have an arbitrarily sharp rate of attenuation, with totally linear phase shift, and hence no group-delay distortion. This class of filter does have a non-digital analog: the comb filter.

A comb filter combines a signal with a time-delayed version of itself. There is total cancellation at all frequencies that are odd multiples of the half wavelength that is equivalent to the time delay. (Remember, a 180-degree phase inversion is the same as delay by half a wavelength.) The frequency response of such a filter will look like a comb, with many zeroes or nulls as one goes up in frequency, with intermediate points showing no attenuation. A transverse filter builds on this concept; taps are taken on a delay line, and many delayed versions of the signal are added together in various proportions. The more taps, the closer it is possible to get to an ideal filter response. Because the best delay lines are digital, it is impossible to build such a filter unless digital techniques are used.

If the signal is first digitized, the time delay can be accomplished with memory chips and a shift register. To add the delayed versions of the signal in various proportions requires multiplication by specific coefficients, followed by addition to derive the filter output. This can be done with a specialized CPU, or computer chip. The digital filters used in CD players can attenuate a signal over 80 dB in the range between 21 and 22 kHz. Such filters require on the order of 100 samples multiplied by an equally large set of coefficients, which are then added together, 44,100 times every second. There are tricks that will reduce the number of calculations by 50%, but this is still an impressive feat. The derivation of the coefficients is not trivial. Many mathematicians spend considerable energy seeking better ways to compute the coefficients.

The digital signal processors for surround sound that are currently on the market could be reconfigured as digital crossovers, and would sell in the same price range, 600 to 800 dollars.

REFERENCES

Jung, Walter G. *IC Op-Amp Cookbook.* Indianapolis, IN: Howard W. Sams & Co., Inc. 1974.

Lancaster, Don. *Active Filter Cookbook.* Indianapolis, IN: Howard W. Sams, Inc. 1975.

Linkwitz, Sigfried H. "Active Crossover Networks for Noncoincident Drivers," *J.A.E.S.,* Jan/Feb 1976, reprinted in *Loudspeakers, An Anthology of Articles on Loudspeakers from the Pages of the Journal of the Audio Engineering Society.* New York, NY: Audio Engineering Society, 1980.

Small, Richard H. "Constant-Voltage Crossover Design," reprinted in *J.A.E.S.,* 1971, and in *Loudspeakers* (see above reference).

10
Speaker Design Programs

THERE WAS A TIME WHEN THE SAFEST WAY TO DESIGN A SPEAKER SYSTEM FOR A GIVEN driver was to use a sealed box, adding fiberglass stuffing until the system didn't sound too boomy. The vented box, known as a "bass reflex," was an unknown mystery, even for the professional engineer. All too many projects that started out as vented boxes became "acoustic suspension," or closed box systems, when the designer found he couldn't get decent sound from the thing any other way. Still, people tried vented boxes, because when they worked, they were more efficient and had more bass than comparable closed-box enclosures.

It was frustration at failing to match a vented box to a given driver, while working on a project for a certain manufacturer, that led Neville Thiele, an Australian engineer, to perform an exhaustive analysis of such systems. He found the vented box to be analogous to an electrical filter network. His paper was published in 1961 in an Australian engineering journal. It remained unknown in the U.S. until 1971, when it was republished in the *Journal of the Audio Engineering Society* due to the efforts of Richard H. Small. The following year Small published a remarkable series of papers building on Thiele's work. These papers are a definitive analysis of closed and vented-box design under both large-signal and small-signal conditions. They are necessary reading for anyone who is serious about designing loudspeakers. (The interested reader is directed to the references at the end of this chapter.)

This chapter's material is based on Thiele's and Small's work, as well as that of others who have contributed to our understanding of loudspeaker design. Detailed anal-

1 inch	= 25.4 millimeters	
1 centimeter	= 10.0 millimeters	
1 centimeter	= 0.3937 inches	
1 liter	= 0.001 meter^3	
1 liter	= 0.03531 ft^3	
1 liter	= 1000 cm^3	

Table 10-1. Metric Equivalents.

ysis of power-handling capabilities is not covered, though some common sense rules of thumb are discussed. Several computer programs are presented which greatly simplify the necessary calculations. These programs were written in BASIC for Apple II computers, and with only one exception can easily be translated into other BASIC dialects. (The programs are available on disk for Apple II and IBM at a modest charge as a service for those who would find it tedious to key in code. See the Appendix for details.) If you don't have a computer, a calculator with a square-root key can perform many of the calculations.

If you are already familiar with the mechanical aspect of speaker cabinet construction, this chapter will help you design cabinets that match the drivers you wish to use. If you are a tyro at speaker cabinet construction, it is my hope to encourage you to explore the references at the end of this chapter.

A few metric- to foot-pound conversion factors will be useful, because manufacturers may use either to specify parameters. They can be found in Table 10-1.

LOUDSPEAKER PARAMETERS

The loudspeaker itself is known as a *driver* to distinguish it from the loudspeaker system it becomes when mounted in a box. The following driver parameters must be known if one is to design a system rationally:

F_S—Resonant frequency of driver

V_{AS}—The volume of air having the same acoustic compliance as the driver

Q_T—Total driver Q (a measure of sharpness of resonance)

These parameters can be measured (procedures are given in Weems's book, *How to Design, Build & Test Complete Speaker Systems*, now unfortunately out of print, as well as in Small's papers), but the weekend cabinet builder needn't go out of his way to do this, because the Thiele-Small parameters should be readily available. If your dealer won't supply them, find another dealer. All manufacturers publish spec sheets for their products. The dealer should have them available. If the manufacturer doesn't supply at least these three specs, the speaker is an unlikely candidate for high-fidelity applications.

There are also three parameters pertaining to the box:

V_B—Net internal volume of enclosure

F_B—Frequency to which the box is tuned (vented box only)

Q_L—The loss factor caused by box leakage

If the speaker parameters are known, a box can be designed with the proper characteristics, resulting in an acceptable frequency response.

CLOSED-BOX SPEAKER DESIGN

Closed-box design is much easier than vented-box design. There are fewer parameters to worry about, and the final system response is much less sensitive to variations in these parameters. Building a closed box is easier, because constructing and fitting a vent to a cabinet can add several hours to project construction, and will likely require additional tools. Tuning a vent can be time consuming and requires test instruments. Although it can be well worth the trouble with some drivers, others will give excellent performance in a closed box, and some will function well only this way.

Small may have been the first to popularize the notion that a closed box behaves like a second-order filter. The parameter Q_{TS} determines the total system Q. If it is 0.7, the system response is maximally flat, like a Butterworth filter. There are no peaks or excessive drooping in the response curve. In short, the smaller the box, the higher the system's resonant frequency and the higher the Q; thus the bass is "boomier." Enlarge the box, and resonant frequency and Q decrease: bass response becomes flatter. Too large a box, and bass response sags.

Q's as high as one are considered acceptable; they give fuller, more extended bass response, without causing more than a one dB peak in response. Golden-eared purists insist on a Q of 0.7 or even lower to optimize transient response, but lower Q's can result in an excessively large enclosure, poor power-handling capabilities, and distorted sound with some drivers.

The relationship between Q_{TS}, the total system Q, and Q_T, total driver Q (itself a combination of mechanical and electrical Q) is given by

$$Q_{TS} = Q_T \sqrt{\frac{V_{AS}}{V_B} + 1}$$

You can see by examining this equation that the bigger the box (V_B), the lower the total system Q will be. Using a smaller box will raise the Q. Unfortunately, too large a box will reduce the spring effect of the air in the cabinet. The speaker cone won't rebound quickly enough to follow a signal accurately, and distortion will be the result. Power handling will also suffer if the box is too large to help keep the speaker cone in place. If V_{AS} is not larger than V_B, you are almost certain to have trouble.

The system resonance frequency (F_R) follows the same ratio as does the Q:

$$F_R = F_S \sqrt{\frac{V_{AS}}{V_B} + 1}$$

The smaller the box, the higher the system resonance. However, due to the response

Table 10-2. Relationship of Q to Resonant Frequency.

Total System Q	Ratio of Low-Frequency Cutoff (F_3) to System Resonance Frequency	
	0.7	1.0
	0.8	0.89
	0.9	0.83
	1.0	0.79

peak that occurs at resonance, the cutoff point, F_3, will be lower with a smaller box. If total system Q is one, F_3 will be about $\frac{8}{10}$ the resonant frequency, F_R. If Q is .7, the resonant frequency will equal the cutoff frequency (see Table 10.2).

Finding the Proper Box Size

Starting with a given driver, one usually wants to know how big a box to build for it. That is exactly what the program in Fig. 10-1 does, using the following formula derived from the one for total system Q:

$$V_B = V_{AS} / ((Q_{TS}/Q_T) - 1)$$

By plugging in various values to the program, one quickly gains an intuitive understanding of the relationships between the various parameters and how they affect the system response.

Figure 10-2 is a sample run of the program. It finds the box size for a hypothetical speaker with a Q_T of 0.3, a compliance (V_{AS}) equivalent to 19 cubic feet, and a resonance of 20 Hz. For a total system Q of 0.7, a box volume of 4.3 cubic feet will be required. On the other hand, if a system Q of one is acceptable, the box size will be under two cubic feet. The range of box sizes that can produce acceptable sound is so great that it would be hard to build a system that didn't produce acceptable results.

Most speakers would not work well in a box as large as four cubic feet. Our hypothetical speaker would probably work, because its Q_T is so low; this indicates a large magnet, which increases the accuracy with which the speaker cone traces a signal. The air-spring effect of a smaller box isn't required for low distortion. As a rule of thumb, the box's acoustic compliance, V_B, should be less than the speaker's V_{AS}.

The maximally flat alignment will produce a speaker system with resonant and cutoff frequenices of 47 Hz. The Q = 1 alignment produces a speaker with a system resonance of 67 Hz, but a cutoff of 53 Hz. Conventional wisdom dictates that the first speaker would be ideal for classical music, the second for rock and roll. Perhaps, but some intermediate of value Q_{TS} would probably give a more reasonably sized system, without too much emphasis in the bass.

If you decide to build a system using values derived by this program, remember that the speaker itself subtracts volume from the enclosure, as do any supports or braces you add to the box. These can reduce the box size as much as 15%. It will also be neces-

124

```
]LOAD CLOSED BOX SIZE
]LIST

10    HOME
20    PRINT "BOXSIZE FOR A GIVEN S
      PEAKER": PRINT "IN A SEALED
      BOX"
30    PRINT "BY RICHARD KAUFMAN"
40    PRINT "COPYRIGHT (C) 1985"
50    PRINT
60    PRINT "WHAT ARE THE SPEAKER
      PARAMETERS?"
70    PRINT "ENTER VAS, QT, FS"
80    INPUT VAS, QT, FS
90    PRINT "WHAT IS THE DESIRED S
      YSTEM Q": PRINT "  (IDEAL RA
      NGE: .7 < Q < 1)"
100   INPUT TSQ
110   VB = VAS / ((TSQ / QT) ^ 2 -
      1)
120   PRINT "REQUIRED BOX VOLUME
      = ";VB
130   GOSUB 180
140   PRINT "ENTER Y TO RERUN"
150   INPUT ANS$: IF ANS$ = "Y" THEN
      70
160   IF ANS$ = "y" THEN 70
170   PRINT  CHR$ (4)"RUN HELLO"
180   FR = FS * (VAS / VB + 1) ^ .
      5
190   PRINT "SYSTEM RESONANCE = "
      ;FR
200   RETURN
```

Fig. 10-1. Closed-box design program listing.

sary at least to line the box with some fiberglass or polyester fiber stuffing in order to damp internal reflection of higher frequency sound. Such stuffing can add as much as 15 or 20% to the effective volume of the box, but at the cost of system efficiency. (The fibers' movement with variation in air pressure adds to the acoustic compliance within the box.) It is possible to add too much stuffing, packing it so tight that the box becomes acoustically smaller. For most accurate results, you will want to measure the system resonance and adjust it toward the desired value. If you have designed for a value of Q_{TS} that is in the middle of the acceptable range, this won't be necessary. If not, or if you are a perfectionist, here's how to measure system resonance.

```
]LOAD CLOSED BOX SIZE
]RUN
BOXSIZE FOR A GIVEN SPEAKER
IN A SEALED BOX
BY RICHARD KAUFMAN
COPYRIGHT (C) 1985

WHAT ARE THE SPEAKER PARAMETERS?
ENTER VAS, QT, FS
?19
??.3
??20
WHAT IS THE DESIRED SYSTEM Q
   (IDEAL RANGE: .7 < Q < 1)
?.7
REQUIRED BOX VOLUME = 4.275
SYSTEM RESONANCE = 46.6666667
ENTER Y TO RERUN
?Y
ENTER VAS, QT, FS
?19
??.3
??20
WHAT IS THE DESIRED SYSTEM Q
   (IDEAL RANGE: .7 < Q < 1)
?1
REQUIRED BOX VOLUME = 1.87912088
SYSTEM RESONANCE = 66.6666667
ENTER Y TO RERUN
?N
```

Fig. 10-2. Closed-box design program sample run.

——MEASURING A SPEAKER'S RESONANT FREQUENCY——

You will need an audio signal generator and an ac voltmeter or a multimeter. I find analog instruments are easier to read than digital instruments for this test (refer to Fig. 10-3). The output of the signal generator is fed into an amplifier. The amp's output is fed through a 2-watt resistor of any value between 500 and 1000 ohms. (Parallel four ½-watt, 2.2 kilohm resistors if you don't have any 2-watt resistors handy.) Measure the voltage across the speaker terminals as you sweep down in frequency with the signal generator. Set the signal generator so that the signal level across the speaker measures about one volt at higher frequencies, above 150 Hz. As you adjust the generator's output down in frequency, the voltage level will rise to a peak of several volts, then drop again. The frequency at which it peaks is the system's resonant frequency.

If there is no sharp peak, but only a broad plateau instead, this might indicate cabi-

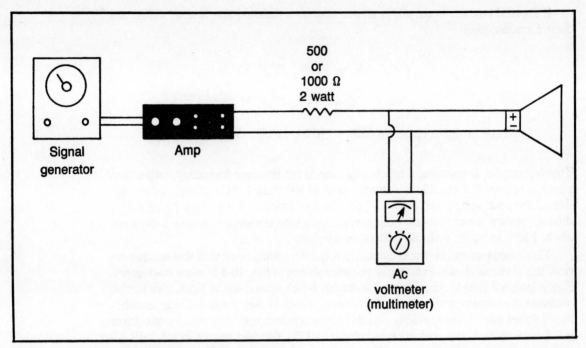

Fig. 10-3. Test setup for measuring system resonance.

net leaks. With the signal generator set to 30 Hz, listen carefully along all cabinet joints and seams for the hissing sound of an air leak. (A stethoscope or a rolled-up piece of paper helps.) Seal any leaks you find with white glue, silicone sealer, or other suitable material. Sometimes the leak will be in the speaker's surround or dust cap. If you can't get a sharp peak, estimate the center point of the plateau and use that figure.

Once you know the system resonance, you can adjust it up or down by removing or adding fiberglass or plastic fiber stuffing. If the box is too large, wooden blocks can be used to decrease its volume.

SPEAKER DESIGN FOR A VENTED BOX

The following formulas were developed by D.B. Keele, Jr., to find box characteristics that will obtain good performance with a given driver:

$$V_B = 15Q_T^{2.87} V_{AS}$$

$$F_3 = 0.26Q_T^{-1.4}F_S$$

$$F_B = 0.42Q_T^{0.9}F_S$$

(F_3 represents the cutoff frequency, where the bass response is down by 3 dB.) The response one gets by following these formulas is known as the *fourth-order Butterworth*, considered by most designers to be optimum. It is flat, with no peaks or dips, and consequently does not sound "boomy."

If the ideal box size is not practical, one may try a different size box, in which case these formulas apply:

$$F_3 = Fs\ (V_{AS}/V_B)^{0.5}$$

$$F_B = Fs\ (V_{AS}/V_B)^{0.32}$$

$$\text{Peak or dip in response (dB)} = 20\ \log\ (2.6Q_T\ (V_{AS}/V_B)^{0.35})$$

If the last number is negative, it represents a dip at the resonant frequency, rather than a peak in response. Generally, a response peak of less than 1 dB is considered acceptable. If the peak occurs well below 50 Hz, then as much as 2 dB might be tolerable, although purists would probably disagree, claiming that transient response suffers too much. I tend to agree with the purists on this issue.

These formulas can be worked out on a scientific calculator or with that antique device, the slide rule, but the computer program shown in Fig. 10-4 is more convenient. Figure 10-5 is a sample run, using a Speakerlab 8-inch driver, the W808P. (Speakerlab publishes the necessary parameters for speaker design in their catalog. Some manufacturers do not make them so readily available.) The optimum enclosure size for this driver is 2.1 cubic feet. A 25% reduction in volume to 1.5 cubic feet results in a 1.1 dB response irregularity. This is a very different situation from the closed box, where reducing box size by over 50% would result in a 1-dB bump in the response curve. Obviously, the vented box is more sensitive to parameter variations.

For speakers with Q_T's greater than 0.6, the program will give very large box sizes and low tuning frequencies. If you try to build such a system, it will have deep bass but high distortion, and poor power-handling capability. It will only play quietly, because the speaker suspension will bottom easily even at moderate listening levels. If the driver's Q_T is over 0.6, use a different driver, or try a closed box, even though its Q can end up as high as 1.1 or 1.2.

Vent Parameters

In order to tune the box to a desired frequency (F_B), a vent of a specific size must be installed. The vent must have an area large enough not to impede air flow, otherwise vent noises such as whistling and chuffing will be heard. Small considers that if maximum air velocity in a vent does not exceed 5% of the speed of sound, vent noise will not be a problem, nor will constriction of the air flow alter the system parameters. His formula, converted from metric units, is

$$S_V = 0.02F_B\ V_D$$

where

S_V = minimum acceptable vent area, in square inches
F_B = Box frequency
V_D = peak volume displacement of the loudspeaker in cubic inches

```
]PR#1
]LOAD VENTED BOX PARMS
]LIST

10    HOME
20    PRINT "SPEAKER BOX DESIGN"
30    PRINT "BY RICHARD KAUFMAN"
40    PRINT "COPYRIGHT (C) 1985"
50    PRINT
60    PRINT "INPUT SPEAKER FS"
70    INPUT FS
80    PRINT "INPUT Q": INPUT Q
90    PRINT "INPUT VAS": INPUT VAS

100 F3 = .26 * Q ^  - 1.4 * FS
110 FB = .42 * Q ^  - .9 * FS
120   PRINT "F3=";F3, "FB=";FB, "VB
      =";15 * Q ^ 2.87 * VAS
130   PRINT "HIT S KEY TO STOP, A
      NY OTHER TO CONTINUE": INPUT
      S$
140   IF S$ < > "S" THEN 160
150   PRINT  CHR$ (4)"RUN HELLO"
160   PRINT "INPUT NEW VB": INPUT
      VB
170 F3 = FS * (VAS / VB) ^ .5
180 FB = FS * (VAS / VB) ^ .32
190 LN = (2.6 * Q * (VAS / VB) ^
      .35)
195 HUMP = 20 *  LOG (LN) /  LOG
      (10)
200   PRINT "F3=";F3, "FB=";FB, "HU
      MP=";HUMP
210   GOTO 130
```

Fig. 10-4. Vented-box speaker design program.

You can calculate the peak volume displacement of a speaker from its diameter and from its maximum cone excursion, X_{MAX}. X_{MAX} is usually the same as voice-coil overhang, which is more often specified by manufacturers. If this figure is not available, the following estimates are safe to use: for 12-inch speakers—12 mm, for 10-inch—6 mm, and for 8-inch drivers—4 mm. Most speakers have an excursion less than these, though an occasional driver will have an overhang that is greater, in which case the manufacturer should boast about it instead of hiding it.

Figure 10-6 is the program that calculates vent area given the box frequency, driver diameter, and X_{MAX}. The sample run in Fig. 10-7 shows a vent area of four square

```
]RUN VENTED BOX PARMS
SPEAKER BOX DESIGN
BY RICHARD KAUFMAN
COPYRIGHT (C) 1985

INPUT SPEAKER FS
?28.5
INPUT Q
?.345
INPUT VAS
?2.97
F3=32.8754325    FB=31.1929871
VB=2.10081839
HIT S KEY TO STOP, ANY OTHER TO CONTINUE
?
INPUT NEW VB
?1.5
F3=40.1030548    FB=35.4631836
HUMP=1.1325052
HIT S KEY TO STOP, ANY OTHER TO CONTINUE
?
INPUT NEW VB
?1.8
F3=36.6089129    FB=33.4533583
HUMP=.578236477
HIT S KEY TO STOP, ANY OTHER TO CONTINUE
?S
```

Fig. 10-5. Vented-box speaker design program sample run.

inches or more to be acceptable for the W806P speaker.

The formula for calculating vent length is

$$L_V = \frac{S_V}{0.00037 V_B F_B^2} - .83 V\, S_V$$

where

L_V = Vent length, in inches
S_V = Vent area, in square inches
F_B = Box frequency
V_B = Box volume, in cubic feet

The program is listed in Fig. 10-8, and the sample run is Fig. 10-9. Remember that the vent area calculated by Small's method is only a recommendation; larger areas are desir-

```
?
]LOAD VENT AREA
]LIST

10   HOME
20   PRINT "VENT AREA CALCULATION
     "
30   PRINT : PRINT "BY RICHARD KA
     UFMAN"
40   PRINT "COPYRIGHT (C) 1986"
50   PRINT
60   PRINT "INPUT BOX FREQUENCY"
70   INPUT FB
80   PRINT "INPUT SPEAKER DIAMETE
     R IN INCHES"
90   INPUT D:A = (D / 2) ^ 2 * 3.
     1416
100  PRINT "INPUT XMAX, MAXIMUM
     DIAPHRAGM": PRINT "      EXC
     URSION IN MILLIMETERS"
110  INPUT XMAX
120  XMAX = XMAX / 25.4
130  VD = XMAX * A
140  SV = .02 * FB * VD
150  PRINT "MINIMUM RECOMMENDED
     VENT AREA = ",SV
160  PRINT : PRINT "HIT ANY KEY
     FOR MENU"
170  INPUT KEY$
180  PRINT  CHR$ (4),"RUN HELLO"
```

Fig. 10-6. Vent area calculation program.

able, particularly at frequencies below 40 Hz. You should use the widest vent that is practical. Three-inch diameter cardboard tubes are readily available from such sources as mailing tubes, carpet roll tubes, and rolls of dry cleaners' bags. The internal area of such tubes is very close to seven inches. The program shows that such a vent must be seven inches long to tune the 2.1 ft.^{3} box to 31.2 Hz. Some authorities say the vent length must never exceed twice its diameter, but I've found that 2.5 times the diameter gives acceptable results. You will probably have to trim the tube's length to obtain a precise tuning. Remember also that the tube subtracts its volume from that of the box. You will have to allow for this in determining your box dimensions.

If you must use a narrower or longer tube than these recommendations, mounting the duct on the back of the cabinet or even underneath it, if the cabinet is on legs, can help attenuate any objectionable noises produced by the vent. (If there is insufficient clearance beneath the cabinet, this will make the vent effectively longer, perhaps nar-

```
]
]LOAD VENT AREA
]RUN
VENT AREA CALCULATION

BY RICHARD KAUFMAN
COPYRIGHT (C) 1986

INPUT BOX FREQUENCY
?31.2
INPUT SPEAKER DIAMETER IN INCHES
?8
INPUT XMAX, MAXIMUM DIAPHRAGM
       EXCURSION IN MILLIMETERS
?3.2
MINIMUM RECOMMENDED VENT AREA =
3.95158859

HIT ANY KEY FOR MENU
```

Fig. 10-7. Vent area calculation program sample run.

rower, affecting the tuning.) Rounding the vent's edges to streamline the air flow can also help.

Tuning a Vented Box

The same test setup used for measuring system resonance in a closed box can be used for measuring F_B, the box frequency. This was shown in Fig. 10-3. Instead of looking for a maximum voltage across the speaker terminals as you change the frequency of the generator, you look for a minimum value, which will occur between two peak values. If the peaks and valley cannot be readily discerned, it is a sign of a leaking enclosure. You should start with a vent that is an inch or two longer than the calculations indicate, gradually shortening it until the desired box frequency is attained.

It also helps to know the exact acoustic size of the enclosure you are working with. Figure 10-10 shows a program to determine if your box is the desired volume for the speaker you are designing. The program uses the driver's V_{AS}, and resonant frequency, F_S, as well as the desired box volume, V_B. The program tells you the resonant frequency of the driver when mounted in a closed box the size of V_B. Knowing what the resonant frequency should be, allows you to adjust the acoustic volume of the box by adding or removing fiberglass or plastic fiber acoustic material, or to use wooden blocks to decrease volume. Simply measure the resonant frequency of the system when the vent is tightly covered so that the box is sealed, and adjust box volume until the resonant frequency is the value given by the program. Remember that the vent's volume will be included in this measurement, so subtract it to figure the actual box volume. After the box size has been adjusted, you might want to retune the vent frequency. Of course

```
LOAD VENT LENGTH
LIST

10    HOME
20    PRINT "VENT LENGTH CALCULATI
      ON"
30    PRINT "BY RICHARD KAUFMAN"
40    PRINT "COPYRIGHT (C) 1985"
50    PRINT
60    PRINT "INPUT BOX FREQUENCY"
70    INPUT FB
80    PRINT "INPUT BOX VOLUME, IN
      CUBIC FEET"
90    INPUT VB
100   PRINT "INPUT VENT AREA, IN
      SQUARE INCHES"
110   INPUT SV
120   ALPHA = .00037 * VB * FB * F
      B
130   LV = SV / ALPHA - .83 *  SQR
      (SV)
140   PRINT "VENT LENGTH = ";LV;"
      INCHES"
150   INPUT "DONE?";AN$
160   IF AN$ = "N" THEN 100
170   PRINT  CHR$ (4),"RUN HELLO"
```

Fig. 10-8. Vent length calculation program.

changing the vent length again will alter the cabinet's size, but the change should be insignificant in terms of system response.

Vented Box Frequency Response

Figure 10-11 shows a program that graphs the frequency response of vented speaker system. You enter the speaker and box parameters, then watch the resulting display. You can overlay several curves for comparison. This program is hardware-dependent because it was written for Apple II graphics, and so cannot be readily adapted to other computers. In order to dump the screen without a special graphics interface card or screen dump program, lines 870 to 1120 dump the screen buffer to the printer, translating characters into printable form. There is no way this will run on another system as written (but see the Appendix).

Skip this paragraph unless you would like to rewrite the screen graphics for a different computer. Lines 640 to 740 form the loop that plots to the Apple's low-res screen, which is 40 × 24 pixels; 40 discrete pixels are plotted, representing frequencies from

```
]PR#1
]LOAD VENT LENGTH
]RUN
VENT LENGTH CALCULATION
BY RICHARD KAUFMAN
COPYRIGHT (C) 1985

INPUT BOX FREQUENCY
?31.2
INPUT BOX VOLUME, IN CUBIC FEET
?2.1
INPUT VENT AREA, IN SQUARE INCHES
?4
VENT LENGTH = 3.62846683 INCHES
DONE?N
INPUT VENT AREA, IN SQUARE INCHES
?7
VENT LENGTH = 7.05884336 INCHES
DONE?Y
```

Fig. 10-9. Vent length calculation program sample run.

```
]
]LOAD RESONANCE IN BOX
]LIST

10   HOME
20   PRINT "SPEAKER RESONANCE IN
     A BOX"
30   PRINT "BY RICHARD KAUFMAN"
40   PRINT "COPYRIGHT (C) 1985"
50   PRINT
60   PRINT "INPUT VAS, VB, FS"
70   INPUT VAS, VB, FS
80 FR = FS * (VAS / VB + 1) ^ .5

90   PRINT "FR=";FR
100  PRINT "ENTER Y TO RERUN"
110  INPUT ANS$: IF ANS$ = "Y" THEN
     60
120  PRINT  CHR$ (4)"RUN HELLO"
```

Fig. 10-10. Program to calculate resonant frequency of a speaker in a box.

```
LOAD GRAPH RESPONSE
LIST

100   REM VARIABLES:
110   REM I = SUBSCRIPT VARIABLE
120   REM TNT = SCREEN COLOR
130   REM II = PARAMETER INDEX
140   REM A,B,C,D = INTERMEDIATE
150   REM             VARIABLES
160   REM FM = FREQUENCY PLOTTED
170   REM G,H,I = INTERMEDIATE
180   REM             VARIABLES
190   REM K = RESPONSE, IN DB
200   REM P$ = PRINT STRING
210   HOME
220   PRINT "*********************
      *"
230   PRINT
234   PRINT "GRAPH OF SPEAKER RES
      PONSE"
240   PRINT "BY RICHARD KAUFMAN"
250   PRINT "COPYRIGHT (C) 1987"
260   PRINT
270   PRINT "*********************
      *"
310   PRINT : PRINT "TO OUTPUT RA
      W DATA TO PRINTER"
320   PRINT "IN SLOT 1, ENTER Y"
330   INPUT AN$
340   IF AN$ < > "Y" THEN 370
350   PRINT : PRINT "TURN ON PRIN
      TER"
360   PRINT  CHR$ (4)"PR#1"
370   GR
380   TNT = 15
390   II = 1
400   COLOR= 1
410   REM *********************

420   REM SET UP AND GET DATA
430   REM *********************

440   FOR I = 3 TO 40 STEP 4: HLIN
      0,39 AT I
450   NEXT
```

Fig. 10-11. Program to graph a vented systems's frequency response.

```
460   COLOR= 2
470   FOR I = 0 TO 39 STEP 5: VLIN
      0,39 AT I: NEXT
480   PRINT "ENTER FS,Q,VAS"
490   INPUT FS,Q,VAS
495   FOR JJ = II TO 5
500 FS(JJ) = FS:Q(JJ) = Q:VAS(JJ
    ) = VAS: NEXT JJ
510   PRINT "ENTER VB,FB,QL"
520   COLOR= TNT
530   INPUT VB,FB,QL
540 VB(II) = VB:FB(II) = FB:QL(I
    I) = QL
550   LET A = FB ^ 2 / FS ^ 2
560 B = A / Q + FB / (QL * FS *
    Q)
570 C = 1 + A + FB / (QL * FS *
    Q) + VAS / VB
580 D = 1 / Q + FB / (QL * FS)
590   REM ******************
600   REM FOLLOWING LOOP
610   REM CALCULATES AND GRAPHS
620   REM SPEAKER RESPONSE
630   REM ******************
640   FOR I = 78 TO 0 STEP  - 2
650 FM = (I + 20) / FS
660 G = FM ^ 4 - C * FM ^ 2 + A
670 H = B * FM - D * FM ^ 3
680 J = FM ^ 4 /  SQR ((G * G) +
    (H * H))
690 K =  LOG (J) /  LOG (10)
700   PRINT (I + 20);" ";.2 *  INT
    (100 * K)
710   IF (40 - (80 * K + 21)) < 1
      THEN  GOTO 740
720   IF (40 - (80 * K + 21)) > 3
    9 THEN  GOTO 740
730   PLOT I / 2,41 - (80 * K + 2
    1)
740   NEXT I
750 TNT = TNT - 1
760   PRINT "TO STOP, ENTER 'Y'":
      INPUT ANS$: IF ANS$ = "Y" THEN
    800
770 II = II + 1
780   IF TNT < 2 THEN TNT = 15
790   COLOR= TNT: GOTO 510
```

```
800   PRINT
810   PRINT "DO YOU WANT TO PRINT
      THE SCREEN? Y OR N"
820   INPUT ANS$: IF ANS$ = "N" THEN
      1070
830   PRINT "TURN ON PRINTER IN S
      LOT#1"
840   REM **********************
      *
850   REM  FOLLOWING PRINTS SCREE
      N
860   REM **********************
      *
870   PR# 1
880   PRINT
890   FOR I = 0 TO 39
900 P$ = ""
910   FOR J = 0 TO 39
920 X =   SCRN( J,I)
930   IF X = 0 THEN 950
940 X = 16 - X
950 X$ =   STR$ (X)
960   IF X$ = "0" THEN X$ = " "
970   IF X$ = "15" THEN X$ = "-"
980   IF X$ = "14" THEN X$ = "!"
990   IF X$ = "13" THEN X$ = "+"
1000   IF X$ = "12" THEN X$ = "<"
1010   IF X$ = "11" THEN X$ = "%"

1020   IF X$ = "10" THEN X$ = "#"

1030 P$ = P$ + X$
1040   NEXT J
1050   PRINT P$;" ";(19 - I) / 4
1060   NEXT I
1070   PRINT "20...30...40...50..
      .60...70...80...90..."
1090   IF ANS$ = "N" THEN 1130
1100   FOR I = 1 TO II: PRINT : PRINT
      I;" FS = ";FS(I);" QT = ";Q(
      I);" VAS = "VAS(I)
1110   PRINT "  VB = ";VB(I);" FB
      = ";FB(I);" QL = ";QL(I)
1120   NEXT
1125   PR# 0
1130   PRINT "HIT ENTER FOR MENU"

1140   INPUT ANS$
```

```
1145   TEXT
1148   PRINT  CHR$ (4)"PR#0"
1150   REM   IF YOU DON'T HAVE A M
       ENU PROGRAM
1160   REM CHANGE NEXT LINE TO "S
       TOP"
1170   PRINT  CHR$ (4)"RUN HELLO"
```

98 to 20 Hz. Line 650 calculates the frequency being plotted as a ratio of the speaker's resonant frequency (allowing for the displacement from zero by 20 Hz), lines 660-670 calculate intermediate variables, line 689 computes the linear response magnitude, and line 690 converts it to a base ten logarithm, (converting from the BASIC natural log function), in order to express the result in decibels. Line 700 prints the result on the bottom of the screen, 710 is a trap to avoid plotting an off-screen value, which would cause a fatal error, and line 720 plots the appropriate screen pixel. When the loop is finished, line 750 changes the screen color in case you decide to overplot the graph with another response curve. You may save the screen to disk with a BSAVE command for later printing with an appropriate utility, or use any other method you can figure out, such as the kludge used in lines 870-1120 to dump the graph to a printer. You will have to become intimately familiar with your computer's screen buffer to do this.

Figure 10-12 is a sample of the output this program produces. It clearly shows that using a smaller than optimum box for a given speaker results in a peak in the response.

If you are interested in writing a similar program for your computer system, the pertinent formulas follow; they are the same formulas that would be used to calculate the response of a fourth-order high-pass filter. First calculate

$A = F_B^2 / F_S^2$

$B = A/Q_T + F_B/ (Q_L F_S)$

$C = 1 + A + F_B / (Q_L Q_T F_S) + V_{AS} /V_B$

$D = 1/Q_T + F_B / (Q_L F_S)$

$F_N = F/F_S$ (F is the frequency at which the response is being calculated)

Then, the response at a given frequency, F, in decibels, will equal 20 times $\log_{10}$ of the following expression:

$$\frac{F_N}{\{ (F_N^4 - CF_N^2 + A)^2 + (BF_N - DF_N^3)^2 \}^{0.5}}$$

Almost all the terms have been defined earlier in this chapter. Only Q_L has not yet been discussed. This represents losses in the cabinet due to friction, leaks, vent inefficiency,

138

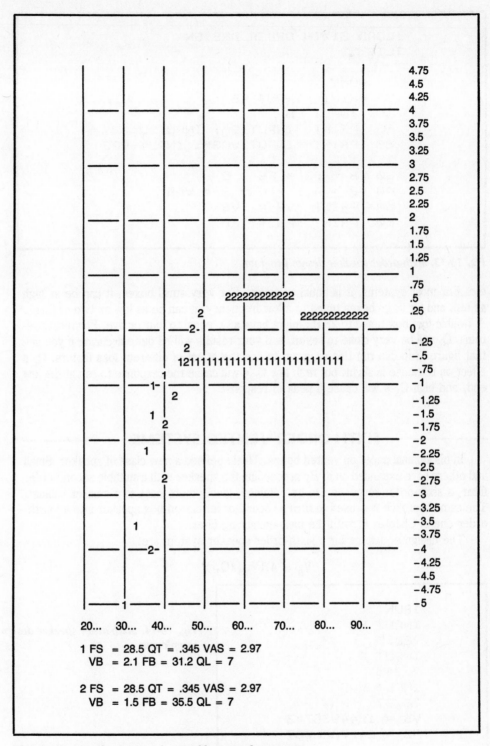

Fig. 10-12. Sample output of vented-box graph program.

```
]LOAD SIXTH ORDER DESIGN
]LIST

1   HOME
5   PRINT "INPUT FS"
10   INPUT FS
15   PRINT "INPUT Q": INPUT Q
20   PRINT "INPUT VAS": INPUT VAS

30 FB = .3 * FS / Q
40 VB = 4.1 * Q ^ 2 * VAS
50   PRINT "VB = "VB
60   PRINT "FB = "FB
```

Fig. 10-13. Sixth-order speaker design program.

etc. For most systems, it is equal to seven. For very small boxes, it can be as high as ten, and for large boxes tuned to a low frequency, it can be as low as two or three. A 4-cubic-foot box tuned to 25 Hz might have a Q_L equal to four or five. For most systems, Q_L will be very close to seven, and your results will be quite accurate if you use that figure. You can run this program to see the effect of different loss factors. Q_L's effect on response is slight, but real: low Q_L's will cause the response to sag at the low end, and high Q_L's will cause a peak in response.

SIXTH-ORDER VENTED SYSTEMS

In his seminal paper on vented boxes, Thiele defined a new class of speaker. Small and others have expanded on it. By preceeding the speaker with a suitable second-order filter, a sixth-order response can be obtained, giving more bass in a smaller cabinet. The same approach was used to turn a second-order closed-box speaker into a fourth-order one in Chapter 8, with the bass-enhancing filter.

The design equations for a sixth-order speaker system are:

$$V_B = 4.1 V_{AS} (Q_T)^2$$

```
]RUN
INPUT FS
?28.5
INPUT Q
?.345
INPUT VAS
?2.97
VB = 1.44936743
FB = 24.7826087
```

Fig. 10-14. Sixth-order speaker design program sample run.

140

$$F_B = 0.3F_S/Q_T$$

The program is shown in Fig. 10-13, the sample run in Fig. 10-14. Using the same W806P speaker as for the vented box, the required box volume is 1.45 cubic feet. The box should be tuned to 24.8 Hz, which will also be the low-frequency cutoff. Excursion-limited power-handling capability will be quite high, because the filter's boost will be applied at frequencies where the vent mass prevents the speaker cone from moving. As long as the speaker has an adequate voice coil, it won't burn out. This alignment is not recommended for all speakers. The ratio of F_S to Q_T should be between 80 and 160 for best results.

The filter should have a resonant frequency that is the same as the box frequency and have a 6-decibel peak; this can be accomplished with a Q of 2 i.e., a damping factor of 0.5. You can modify the bass-enhancing filter of Chapter 8 to meet this requirement. Referring to Fig. 8-12, replace R5 with a 22-kilohm, and R6 with a 33-kilohm, resistor. All that remains is to adjust the pots to a 24.8-Hz resonance for this example. If you want to replace the pots with fixed resistors, the necessary design information is in Chapter 8.

The only remaining problem is to tune the box. With small boxes at low frequencies, you will sometimes find that the required length of duct will not fit in the box. Try using a narrower duct; it can be shorter than a wider one for the same frequency. Of course, vent noise may become a problem. The tricks mentioned earlier in this chapter under the heading of vent design might help. There is also no reason not to mount the duct outside the box, unless you find the results aesthetically disturbing.

REFERENCES

Colloms, Martin. *High-Performance Loudspeakers*, 2nd ed. Devon, England: Pentech Press, 1980.

Small, Richard H. "Closed Box Loudspeaker Systems", Parts I & II, reprinted in *Loudspeakers, An Anthology of Articles on Loudspeakers from the Pages of the Journal of the Audio Engineering Society*, New York, NY: Audio Engineering Society, 1980.

Small, Richard H. "Vented-Box Loudspeaker Systems", Parts I-IV, reprinted in *Loudspeakers* (see above).

Thiele, A. N. "Loudspeakers in Vented Boxes", Parts I & II, reprinted in *Loudspeakers* (see above).

Weems, David B. *How to Design, Build, and Test Complete Speaker Systems*. Blue Ridge Summit, PA: TAB Books, 1978 (out of print).

Weems, David B. *Building Speaker Enclosures*. Blue Ridge Summit, PA: TAB Books, 1981.

Speaker Builder Magazine, published by Edward T. Dell, Jr., PO Box 576, Peterborough, NH 03458, has many interesting speaker construction articles at all levels. Back issues are also available.

11

FM Antennas

"FM" STANDS FOR "FREE MUSIC." IN MOST AREAS, THERE ARE SEVERAL FM stations that play music worth listening to; compact disks as a signal source can make the sound quality superb. If you have ever been lucky enough to hear a live broadcast with good reception, you know how transparent a medium FM radio can be. Unfortunately, most of us never get good reception. A better antenna than the piece of wire that comes with the receiver can change that. The quality of the receiver makes a difference, too, but a $200 receiver can outperform a $600 tuner if the former has a sensitive antenna and the latter is working from a wire draped on the floor.

Just adding an antenna amplifier to a poor antenna does more harm than good. It increases noise level as well as signal level, and does nothing to eliminate interference. A good antenna will increase signal strength without increasing noise, and may be chosen for directional characteristics that will eliminate interference. Requirements for antennas differ, depending on your circumstances. The city dweller in a crowded apartment with no roof access needs an entirely different kind of antenna than the cattle rancher a hundred miles from the nearest station. Both situations will be addressed, and so will conditions between these extremes.

AN IMPROVED DIPOLE

Every manufacturer includes a free antenna with his receiver or tuner, usually a "folded dipole" made of flat TV ribbon wire. Most people just drape them behind their equipment, and if they live near enough to a major population center, they tolerate the

142

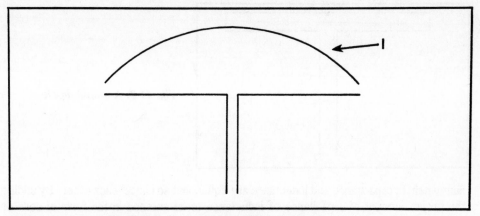

Fig. 11-1. Current distribution on a resonant dipole antenna.

result. That it works at all is due to the magnificent technology of the receivers, not to any virtue of the antenna. Even if a folded dipole were properly spread out and oriented, it still would be limited by a major design flaw built into every one of these antennas. A little theory will explain the problem, which can easily be fixed with a sharp knife, a soldering iron, and some wire.

A dipole is the most basic antenna. The results are best if this antenna is resonant at its intended frequency of operation, so that it can efficiently transfer energy into a transmission line. This is illustrated in Fig. 11-1. The curved line labeled "I" represents the current distribution on the dipole. (This current is caused by the radio wave the antenna receives.) It forms a standing wave that is at a maximum in the center of the line, even though the current's direction is changing millions of times each second. If you try to operate the antenna at another frequency than its length will allow, the current will not form a null at the ends, and energy will be reflected back along the antenna, interfering with the incoming radio wave. This is illustrated in Fig. 11-2. The current will no longer be as strong as possible at the center feed point, and signal strength will suffer. The audible effect on an FM signal will be noise. Technically, an antenna is reso-

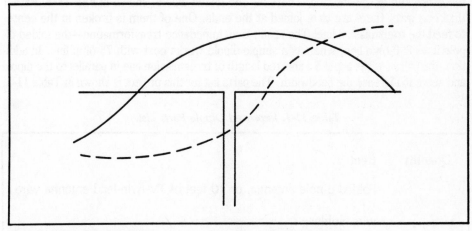

Fig. 11-2. Current distribution on a non-resonant dipole antenna.

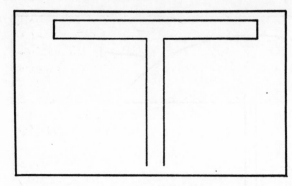

Fig. 11-3. A folded dipole.

nant when its capacitance and inductance are equal, and so cancel each other. By adding the proper amount of capacitance or inductance to an antenna in the form of coils or capacitors, it's possible to tune any length of wire to resonance.

The length of an electromagnetic half-wave in space is given by the formula:

$$L \text{ (in inches)} = 5904/f \text{ (in megahertz)}$$

However, due to capacitive effects at the ends of a wire, the actual length required to build an antenna is about 5% less than this. Thus the formula,

$$L \text{ (in inches)} = 5616/f \text{ (in megahertz)}$$

will give the actual length of wire needed to build a half-wave dipole. At 98 MHz, the center of the FM band, this works out to a length of 57.3 inches. Each half of the antenna should be about 28.5 inches long.

The astute reader will notice that the FM band extends from 88 to 108 MHz. The dipole antenna has problems at either end of the band. At 88 MHz, the antenna halves should be 31.9 inches long, and at 108 MHz 26 inches is the proper length. Reception with a simple dipole will be poorer for those stations further from 98 MHz. It would be nice if there were some way to give those stations a break by somehow increasing the bandwidth of the antenna. There is—the folded dipole, shown in Fig. 11-3. Rather than one wire, there are two, joined at the ends. One of them is broken in the center to feed the transmission line. The result is an impedance transformation—the folded dipole uses 300-ohm line, whereas a simple dipole works best with 75-ohm line. In addition, the paired wires act like a shorted length of transmission line in parallel to the dipole and serve to increase the bandwidth. The parts list for this project is shown in Table 11-1.

Table 11-1. Improved Dipole Parts List.

Quantity	Item
1	Folded dipole antenna, or 10 feet of TV twin-lead antenna wire
—	wire, solder

144

Besides seeing a dipole, your receiver "sees" the reactance due to the shorted transmission line that forms the folded dipole. It works like this: an antenna that is too short acts like a capacitor, whereas a shorted length of transmission line that is less than a quarter-wave in length acts like an inductor. These two reactances have opposite signs and so tend to cancel, keeping the antenna resonant. Conversely, an antenna that is too long acts like an inductor, and a shorted transmission line that is too long acts like a capacitor. Once again, the reactances cancel. In theory, a folded dipole is a self-compensating system that stays tuned at resonance or a broader range of frequencies than an ordinary dipole.

This would be the case if the shorted transmission line were really one-quarter wavelength long. This could be accomplished if open air line were used to build the antenna, but TV twin-lead is the material that is used. The plastic dielectric slows down the radio wave as it travels along such a transmission line, increasing the line's effective length. The percentage by which the radio wave is slowed is called the *velocity factor;* the line must be shortened by the same factor to maintain resonance. The velocity factor for twin-lead line is 80%. Although it slows down radio waves flowing on the antenna in a transmission line mode, the dielectric does not slow down the free-space radio waves it is receiving. That is why the dipole length and transmission-line length are not the same.

The folded dipoles that come with FM receivers are the right length, but the short on the end should be 24 inches from the center of the antenna, as shown in Fig. 11-4, rather than at the ends. Such an antenna can easily be made from TV antenna wire, or else an existing antenna can be modified by scraping off some of the insulation and soldering a short between the wires 24 inches from the center point. Leaving the far ends joined by the existing short doesn't affect the antenna: the ends may be either joined or shorted.

If you just leave your improved, folded dipole draped behind your equipment, you will not be getting the best possible performance from it. Tacking it to the wall can help, but it might still suffer this way. The proximity of the wall will adversely affect the antenna, especially if there is any metal in the wall, such as the foil vapor barrier on the

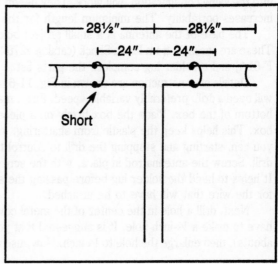

Fig. 11-4. Proper construction of a folded dipole FM antenna from TV twin-lead wire.

28½" — 28½"

24" — 24"

Short

145

external walls of all recent construction. The metal studs used in new buildings don't help, either. You can try putting the antenna across a window, though a screen can make this a poor choice, too. Taping the antenna to a broom handle, then suspending it from the ceiling by strings, or between two pieces of furniture, would be the best way to get optimum performance from a dipole. (Married men who try this may be risking their wives' ire.) If you have to go to these extremes to get good reception, the next antenna might be a better choice.

A VERTICAL GROUND-PLANE ANTENNA

Years ago, all FM stations used horizontal polarization, which meant it was necessary to use a horizontal antenna for reception, or suffer a 10- to 20-dB loss in signal strength. Now, most stations use circular polarization, which works with both horizontal and vertical antennas.

Tethered to the tuner by coaxial cable, this vertical antenna can be moved about the room to find the spot for best reception, and put neatly out of the way when not in use. I have found this antenna to be much more sensitive than the usual wire dipole. Perhaps this is due to the fact that it is free-standing. Because the vertical ground-plane antenna is so easy to move around, you can usually find a position where reception is strong and noise-free. Even a few feet can make a big difference; the same spot doesn't work for different stations, even when they share the same transmitting antenna.

This is a variation on a vertical quarter-wave antenna. Usually the ground-plane is horizontal, but here the rods that form the ground-plane are pointed downward (see Fig. 11-5). This increases the impedance from 50 to 70 ohms, which is better-suited to FM tuners, and also allows the rods to serve as the legs of a tripod to support the base of the antenna.

The antenna itself is made from the same kind of rod as the legs. I have used collapsible replacement antenna rods, which are available from most radio-TV supply shops, as well as at Radio Shack (catalog #270-1401). An even less expensive mail-order source can be found in the Appendix. Any metal rod, even a coat hanger which can be worked into the same configuration, will work. They needn't be telescoping, though this greatly increases portability. The minimum length for the rods is 28 inches.

The base of the antenna is a small project box, a plastic case with a metal cover. These are available from Radio Shack (catalog #270-230). A coax chassis connector, type F-61A, and a solder lug complete the parts list.

Details of construction are shown in Fig. 11-6, and the parts list in Table 11-2. You will need a drill, preferably variable-speed. First, make a hole in the center of the plastic bottom of the box. Place the box firmly on a piece of wood, and drill from inside the box. This helps keep the plastic from shattering, as does using the slowest drill speed you can, starting and stopping the drill to control the speed if you have a fixed-speed drill. Screw the antenna rod in place, with the screw and the solder lug inside the box. It helps to bend the solder lug before passing the screw through it, to allow clearance for the wire that will have to be attached.

Next, drill a hole in the center of the metal cover for the coax connector. You will have to make a ⅜-inch hole. It is suggested that you start with a ⅛-inch bit (or thereabouts), then enlarge the hole to ¼ inch. Now, use a ⅜-inch bit. (If you don't have one,

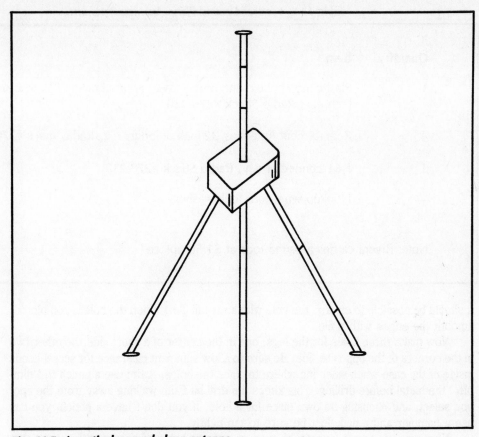

Fig. 11-5. A vertical ground-plane antenna.

Fig. 11-6. Detail of internal construction of the vertical ground-plane antenna.

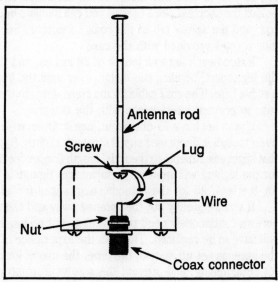

Antenna rod

Screw

Lug

Wire

Nut

Coax connector

Table 11-2. Vertical Ground-Plane Antenna Parts List.

Quantity	Item
1	Plastic project box with metal cover, approximately 3¼ × 2⅛ × 1⅛ inch e.g., Radio Shack #270-230
4	Replacement Antennas, 32 inch or longer e.g., Radio Shack #270-1402
1	F-61 connector e.g., Radio Shack #278-212
—	Hookup wire, four lock-washers

Note: Rivera carries antenna rods at $1.50 apiece

it should be possible to enlarge the hole with a rat-tail file.) When the hole is completed, smooth the edges with a file.

Now make three holes for the legs, one in the center of a short side, the other two in the corners of the opposite side. Be sure to allow sufficient clearance for screw heads inside of the case when selecting where to place the holes. A tip: use a punch to "dimple" the metal before drilling. This keeps the drill bit from walking away from the spot you select, and choosing its own place for a hole. If you don't have a punch, you can use a hammer and a nail. Just be sure to tap lightly.

Now pass the coax connector through the center hole and secure with the nut that comes with it. The nut should be on the inside of the box. Attach the legs securely. Solder the shortest piece of wire you can manage between the solder lug on the antenna rod, and the solder tab of the coax connector. Secure the cover to the box with the four screws provided with the case.

Extend each leg to a length of 28 inches, and the antenna rod to 27. Gently force the legs apart, bending the metal cover until the legs splay out just enough to provide a stable base. The coax cable should come down to the floor before beginning its horizontal run, to prevent interference with the antenna.

If your set has a 75-ohm input, use it. Otherwise, you will need a balun transformer, even though it decreases signal strength slightly (typically one dB). You might also find that slight adjustments to the rods' length (longer for the lower numbered stations, shorter for the higher) will improve performance, though in my situation one length, 29 inches for the legs, 28 for the antenna, works well for all the stations I listen to.

If you frequently put the antenna away and then set it up again, you might find the screws continuously need retightening, but no longer hold after a year's use; the rods will have to be replaced. This was the experience of a friend of mine. If you can't leave the antenna set up most of the time, the use of lockwashers should eliminate the need for retightening, and prevent the screws from stripping their threads.

END-FED HALF-WAVE ANTENNA

The end-fed half-wave antenna, also known as a J-pole, has a bit more gain than the vertical ground-plane antenna, and is very sturdy. It can be built very easily from electrical conduit, fittings, and a junction box. These materials are not to everyone's taste for room decor, though in your den that should be no problem. The antenna can be made with chrome or polished brass tubing for a finished look, though at greater expense. You could mount the antenna in an attic. I tried to convince my wife that this antenna was a post-modern sculpture, but she doesn't like post-modern sculpture, either. Yet beauty is in the eye of the beholder, and this beauty has a bit more gain than the quarter-wave vertical of the last section. Because an end-fed half-wave antenna constricts its reception more into the horizontal plane than does the quarter-wave vertical, this antenna is less vulnerable to interference from such sources as overhead air traffic. Because of the end-feed and the quarter-wave matching section, it is less sensitive to the proximity of the ground than any of the other antennas presented here, and so should be the first choice of those living in ground floor apartments. I found it an excellent overall performer.

Figure 11-7 shows the antenna's construction. Table 11-3 gives the parts list. It is made from ½-inch electrical (EMT) conduit. These tubes come in 10-foot lengths. You will also need a 4-inch junction-box with ½-inch knockouts, two fittings, called EMT-connectors, and one cable-connector for feeding the coax into the junction box. A piece of plywood at least one foot square will provide a sufficiently sturdy base. Note: in-the-wall junction boxes have sharp edges. Use an exterior mounting box with smooth edges. Most hardware stores should stock these materials.

Cut the 10-foot conduit into two pieces, one 90 inches, the other 30 inches long. Use a tubing cutter or a hacksaw. The short tube forms half of the quarter-wave matching section; the long tube forms both the half-wave antenna and the other half of the matching section. Mount the conduit rods, using knockouts that are in diagonal rather than in adjacent corners, in order to get a greater distance between the rods' centers, and to help keep the antenna balanced. You will want to mount the junction box to the base before permanently affixing the coax cable, in order to find the ideal feedpoint. You can use the cover-plate mounting holes in the junction box, obtaining long enough machine screws with flat heads to pass through the plywood and catch the threads in the junction box. Either use flat-head screws or feet on the base to hold it off the floor. You may skip the feedpoint tuning procedure and use the dimensions given in the diagram instead. They gave good results on my prototype, but a different feed-point might work better for you.

To tune the feedpoint, first strip enough insulation from the coax so that the inner conductor can make contact with one rod while the ground shield makes contact with the other. (It doesn't seem to matter which one touches which rod.) Listening to your tuner to gauge signal strength and quality, vary the height at which the coax connection is made, finding the point that gives the best signal for the stations you are most interested in receiving. The point will probably be between three and four inches from the junction box, though construction details can cause it to vary considerably. You may wrap the wire tightly around the rods to keep it from slipping while you perform your tests. This should give an adequate, if temporary, electrical connection.

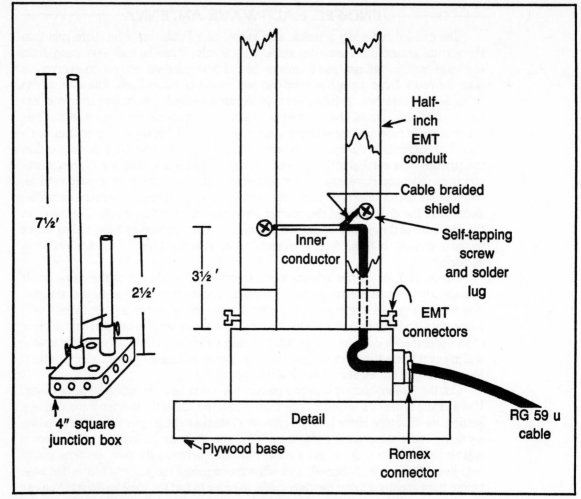

Fig. 11-7. *The end-fed half-wave antenna and construction details.*

After you've found the best feed-point, remove the base, mount the cable connector, and feed the coax into the box. You will have to drill holes in the conduit for screws to hold the wire, and to pass the coax wire through. It is easiest to remove the rods to work on them. I found that using a hacksaw to make a groove enabled the drill bit to make a hole in the conduit. A punch doesn't work very well on a curved surface. You will need one hole large enough to pass the cable through, insulation and all. Take care that the inner connector only touches one of the rods. Two other holes, one in each rod, will be needed for self-tapping screws to fasten the coax wire. Use the screws to hold solder lugs, and solder the wires to them.

─────A CIRCULARLY-POLARIZED DOUBLE LOOP─────

An omnidirectional antenna does not discriminate against signals from any direction, which is an advantage when stations are scattered about the points of the compass. Both

Table 11-3. End-Fed Half-Wave Antenna Parts List.

Quantity	Item
1	Ten-foot length of ½-inch EMT conduit
2	½-inch EMT connectors
1	ROMEX or cable clamp connector
1	Four-inch square surface mount junction box with ½-inch knockouts
1	1-foot × 1-foot × ¾-inch plywood base (or similar)
2	flat-head screws to attach base to junction box #14 self-tapping sheet metal screws, 1-inch long, may be used if machine screws are unavailable
2	¼-inch #14 pan-head sheet metal screws
2	Solder lugs
10 feet (or more)	RG-59 Coax cable

the quarter-wave and half-wave antennas are omnidirectional. But the advantage becomes a handicap in the face of multipath distortion.

Multipath is caused by reflected radio waves. A mountain, a building, even a low cloud can reflect radio waves. The reflected wave arrives at the receiving antenna a split second after the wave following the direct path. The interference between these two waves causes audible noise in the received signal. Because the $R-L$ signal in a multiplex transmission is more easily affected than the $R+L$ signal, stereo reception might be noisy, while monophonic reception is clear (see Chapter 7 on FM noise reduction). If you can get a clear monophonic signal on a station, but reception is noisy when you switch back to stereo, you need an antenna that will discriminate against multipath signals.

The usual advice is to get a directional rooftop antenna, and point it in a direction where it can get the direct signal, and discriminate against the reflected signal(s). This seldom works as well as might be hoped. All too often, the multipath signals are in almost the same direction as the direct signals, and a directional antenna's angular discrimination just isn't sufficient to separate the two. A few years ago that would have been the end of the matter, but a recent change in the way signals are transmitted makes it possible to eliminate multipath signals even when they are in the same direction as the direct signal. Once most FM signals were horizontally polarized, except for a few commuter-oriented stations that used vertical polarization so that a car's vertical antenna would get optimum reception. Now the FCC allows stations to use circular polarization, which can be received by both types of antenna.

To understand polarization, remember that a radio wave is composed of a magnetic field, and an electric field, both perpendicular to each other and to the direction in which the wave is traveling. If the wave is horizontally polarized, the electric currents are horizontal, and a horizontal wire, broadside to the transmitter, will pick up the signal. Likewise for a vertically polarized signal.

A circularly polarized wave will rotate as it travels, like a corkscrew: the polarization will change from horizontal to vertical with the passage of one quarter the wave's period of oscillation, i.e., every quarter wavelength. To complicate things slightly, the wave can have right-hand or left-hand polarization. If an antenna is circularly polarized in the right-hand (clockwise) sense, it will receive vertically, horizontally, and right-hand circularly-polarized signals, but it will discriminate against left-hand circularly-polarized signals.

When a right-hand circularly-polarized signal bounces off an obstacle, it changes its polarization sense and becomes left-hand polarized. The circularly-polarized receiving antenna will discriminate against it, even if it is coming from the same direction as the main signal. Unfortunately, there is no standard for polarization sense for FM transmissions, though the antennas I've seen, and the transmissions I've received in the New York area, all appear to have a right-hand sense.

A one-wavelength loop antenna is a piece of tubing or wire, one wavelength long, broken at one point where it feeds a transmission line. Its polarization is horizontal if the feed point is at the bottom of the loop, and vertical if the feedpoint is on the side. If two loops, one with vertical, one with horizontal sense, are connected by a phasing harness, (a section of transmission line, one-quarter wave in length,) the result is a circularly polarized antenna. The circularly-polarized double loop is shown in Fig. 11-8, and Table 11-4 gives the parts list. As actually constructed, the loops are diagonally polarized, but at right angles to each other. My wife called this antenna the eggbeater; it does bear a certain resemblance to the kitchen utensil.

A single loop of wire, one wavelength long, is resonant. It is bidirectionally sensitive. No signal is received in the plane of the loop, but the loop will have about two decibels of gain for signals that are broadside to it in either direction. For the midpoint of the FM band at 98 megahertz, the loop should have a circumference of 120 inches, or 10 feet. The diameter is 38.2 inches.

The impedance of a circular loop is approximately 160 ohms, which is an awkward value to match to a receiver's 75-ohm input. Two loops in parallel will have an 80-ohm impedance, which is a close enough match to 75-ohm cable.

The problem is to connect the two loops together with a cable having 160-ohm impedance. Your local electronics store does not stock such a cable, but you can make one from two equal lengths of 75-ohm RG-59 cable. The trick is to connect the shields of both cables at either end, as shown in Fig. 11-9. Now the effective impedance between the inner conductors is 150 ohms, which is close enough. In order to make this line an electrical quarter-wave in length, you must take into account the velocity factor of the line.

The presence of a dielectric slows down the radio wave as it travels along a transmission line. Radio Shack specifies the velocity factor of their RG-59 cable as 75%; another type of RG-59 cable, with a different dielectric, could have a velocity factor of 66.7%, or some other number. Assuming a 75% velocity factor, the proper length of the phas-

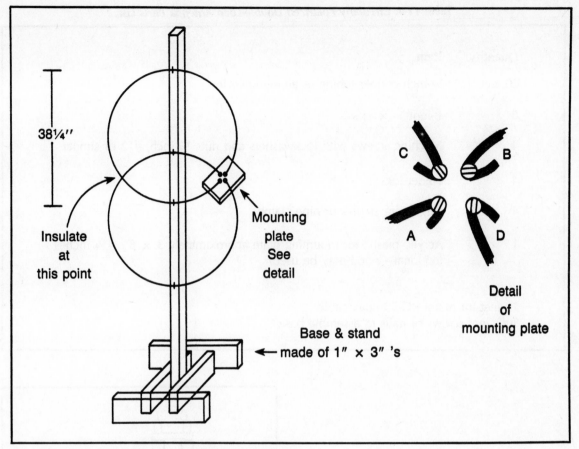

38¼″

Insulate
at
this point

Mounting
plate
See
detail

C   B

A   D

Detail
of
mounting plate

Base & stand
← made of 1″ × 3″ 's

Fig. 11-8. The circularly-polarized double-loop antenna.

ing line connecting the two loops should be 21⅜ inches. This line should be coiled as tightly as possible. Use plastic cable ties, (Radio Shack #278-1632) or plastic tape to hold the line in a coiled position.

Referring to the detail of Fig. 11-8: the mounting plate to which the loops are attached should be a piece of plexiglass or other plastic material. Wood tends to absorb water, become conducting, and interfere with the antenna's function, but it can be used temporarily. Connect the two inner conductors of the phasing harness to solder lugs at points A and B. Connect the other ends to the points marked C and D. Also connect the 75-ohm cable that feeds the tuner, to the points marked C and D. This is a balanced to unbalanced connection. Rather than building a one-to-one balun transformer to transform the balanced antenna terminals to the unbalanced line, tightly coil the transmission line for three turns, as was done for the phasing line. This will tend to "choke" currents on the coax shield, a function which the transformer would otherwise perform. Run the line to the wooden support, and fasten it with cable clips (Radio Shack #20-192) or with insulated staples, for support. Run it down the support to the base, then to the tuner.

The antenna will have a right-hand sense in one direction, and left-hand in the other.

Table 11-4. Circularly Polarized Double-Loop Antenna Parts List.

Quantity	Item
20 feet	¼-inch copper tubing or aluminum wire
2	8-foot 1- × -3's
4	Machine screws with lockwashers and nuts ½ inch, #12 or similar
4	Solder lugs
4	Large wire staples or pipe clamps
1	Acrylic plastic for mounting plate approximately 3 × 3 × ¼ inches (optional—wood may be used)

10 feet (or more) RG-59 coax cable
Sufficient screws or nails to assemble base

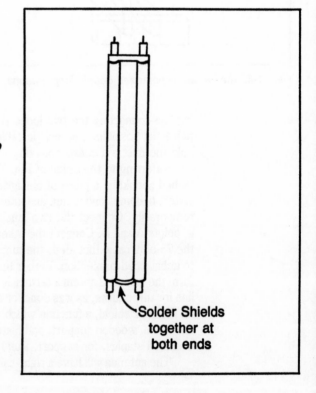

Fig. 11-9. How to make a 150-ohm cable from two lengths of RG-59U cable.

Solder Shields
together at
both ends

Which is which will depend on how the phasing harness is connected. You will have to experiment with the orientation to find out how to get the best reception for the stations you are interested in.

The support and base were built of one-by-threes, held together with nails. Screws would be more durable, and less likely to split the wood. The dimensions are not critical, but the base must be large enough to assure stability. At a minimum, one foot sections are recommended. If you use carriage-bolts and wing-nuts to attach the base to the upright support, it will be possible to store the antenna behind a wall unit when not in use. The loops were made from #8 aluminum wire (Radio Shack #15-035). A more durable antenna could be made using quarter-inch or even ⅜-inch copper tubing, sold wherever they carry plumbing supplies. Your first efforts to form the wire or tubing will probably meet with frustration, for if straightened, tubing has a tendency to kink. The method I hit upon was this: The material comes in rolls. Rather than trying to staighten it, then rebend it into a circle, I took a circle in my hand, and gradually enlarged it by slowly spreading the circle apart.

You will have to keep the two loops from making contact where they cross, as indicated in Fig. 11-8. PVC electrical tape will meet this requirement. The antenna can be adapted to outdoor use, though weatherproofing and more durable construction techniques are recommended if it is to survive a storm. If you try this antenna outdoors, use a grounding block (Radio Shack #15-909) to prevent lightning damage to your equipment or home.

Overall, this antenna has about four dB gain over a dipole, but it seems like more. My apartment house is hemmed in by other tall steel-framed buildings. Multipath is horrendous. The double-loop cleaned it up completely on most stations. Of course, design was optimized for the center of the FM band. Had the dimensions been chosen for a specific station's frequency, I believe all signs of multipath could have been eliminated. As it was, such interference was low enough as not to interfere with serious listening on any station, once the proper orientation was found for the antenna.

HELICAL ANTENNAS

A helical antenna is circularly polarized and has a very wide bandwidth, so it can reject multipath equally well throughout the FM band. The double-loop could be called an indoor antenna only by stretching a point. The helical corkscrew is the same 38 inch diameter as a single loop, but the smallest worthwhile FM helix is 7.5 feet long, and requires a ground screen that is eight-feet square. You will need lots of room for such an antenna, and a sturdy mast to mount it. I have not had the luxury of experimenting with a finished design, but will present the proper design information here. If you live in a mountainous area, distant from most stations you want to hear, this could be the best antenna you can use.

Figure 11-10 shows the physical dimensions of a helical antenna for FM reception, designed for 98 megahertz. The bandwidth of the helix, with the impedance matching method used here, is 40%, which covers the entire FM band. It will not be worth the effort to scale the antenna for a specific station. The number of turns to the helix is arbitrary; three is the minimum worth bothering with, and eight is probably the largest number that it will be practical to build. An eight-turn helix would be 20 feet long. The

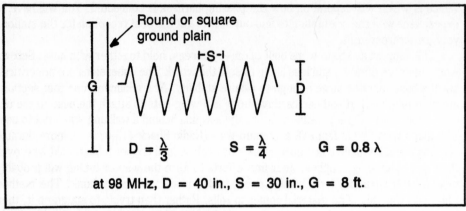

Fig. 11-10. Dimensions for a helical antenna.

gain of this antenna will be approximately two dB per turn, i.e., six dB for three turns, 16 dB for eight. The Greek letter lambda in Fig. 11-10 stands for wavelength, which is 10 feet at 98 mHz. All the other dimensions follow. The diameter of the corkscrew's turns should be 40 inches, the spacing between turns should be 30. The ground plane should be a minimum of eight feet in diameter, or it can be a square eight feet on a side, which is easier to build.

The parts list for helical antenna is shown in Table 11-5. The diameter of the wire used to form the antenna is not critical. The usual recommendation is 0.017 times the wavelength, which would be two inches, an impractical figure unless you work with muffler pipe. Actually, because the bandwidth of a helix is so great, much smaller diameter wire should be okay; experiments I have done tend to bear this out. Although aluminum wire is easy to form, I don't recommend it because it will not be easy to fasten it to the coax connector on the ground screen. Copper tubing, purchased at a hardware store or plumbing supply house, will be ideal, though you should coat it with a protective coat of transparent acrylic spray-paint to resist corrosion when the antenna is completed. Either ¼-, ⅜- or ½-inch tubing may be used.

Hardware cloth is the material most frequently used for a ground screen, but any wire mesh material will do. A lightweight wooden frame will help stabilize the screen. Several pieces of hardware cloth will have to be used to attain the requisite eight-foot width. They should make good electrical contact. Solder or weld them together at several points, and try to form a good mechanical bond as well by twisting and crimping individual wires together.

A coax connector is used on the ground screen to attach 75-ohm cable to the antenna (see Fig. 11-11). BNC connectors are superior to the usual TV/FM type connector in that they are water-proof and provide a lower resistance connection. If you use an F-61 connector instead, water-proof it with a liberal application of silicone sealer and PVC tape when you are finished soldering, and again when the coax is fastened to the finished antenna. The UG-1094 female BNC-connector is superior, as is the matching 75-ohm, UG-88 male connector, but it is hard to find a UG-88 for RG-6U cable. RG-6 cable has lower resistance and less signal loss than RG-59U cable, and is clearly the best choice if the antenna transmission line must be longer than 40 or 50 feet in length.

Table 11-5. Helical Antennas Parts List.

Quantity	Item
30 to 70 feet copper tubing, between ¼ and ⅜ inch diameter (see text)	
4	Ten-foot lengths of 1- × -2's, or similar, for ground-plane support
10 square feet of hardware cloth for ground-plane	
2	Aluminum plates, approximate dimensions: 3 × 3 × ⅛
1	F-61 or BNC 1094 connector
4	Machine screws, nuts, and lockwashers of a size sufficient to affix aluminum plates to ground screen
2	Plastic insulators to support tubing over ground screen (see text for permissible dimensions)
2	Wood or plastic horizontal supports, e.g., 2-inch plastic pipe, length dependent on size of antenna
1	Wood or plastic vertical support, 10 feet or more in length, e.g., 1½-inch diameter oak pole
—	Polypropylene rope for truss, eyebolts for attaching truss

Note: RIVERA carries balun transformers for $1, outdoor baluns and signal combiners for $2, as well as other hardware for use with coax cable.

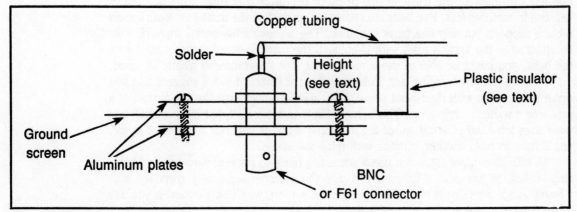

Fig. 11-11. Coupling the helix to a coax line.

The natural impedance of a helix ranges between 140 and 160 ohms, depending on frequency, and exact length of the wire that forms the corkscrew. Matching that value to a 75 ohm line is based on the fact that a wire or tube over a ground plane has an impedance:

$$Z = 138 \log(4h/d)$$

where "h" is the height of the wire over the ground plane, and "d" is the diameter of the wire. As the wire swoops away from the ground plane, its impedance is transformed from 75 ohms to the 160-ohm value of the helix. For quarter-inch tubing, the height should be $\frac{7}{64}$ inch; for $\frac{3}{8}$-inch tubing, "h" is $\frac{5}{32}$ inch, and for $\frac{1}{2}$-inch tubing, "h" is $\frac{7}{32}$. You can shorten or extend the height of the coax fitting appropriately for the diameter of tubing you will be using. To extend the length, solder a piece of 12-gauge copper wire to the connector. The height of the tubing above the ground plane should be constant for six inches, then increase by two inches for the next foot, then it may spiral to the same degree as the rest of the helix.

You will want to solder the tubing to the connector or wire. This is one case where a 30-watt iron just won't get hot enough. A 100-watt heavy-duty iron might do the trick, but I used a butane torch with a soldering tip. Covering the solder joint with silicone sealer will protect it from corrosion.

The method for forming the tubing is to enlarge the circles the tubing comes wound in, rather than trying to straighten the tubing and then rebend it, because the material has an annoying tendency to kink if straightened.

Some form of support will be needed for the coil. Wooden poles, bamboo, fiberglass, PVC plumbing pipe, or two-by-threes are all possibilities, but the lighter and stronger the material, the better. One horizontal might be sufficient, but two will be stronger. Figure 11-12 shows the recommended method of support. The tubing may be fastened to a wooden support with copper pipe clamps, but you will get better results if it is held away from wood with plastic insulating spacers. The usual method of fastening the tubing to plastic poles or pipes is to lash it with nylon fishing line, then wrap with water-proof plastic tape. Some of these boom materials might sag, particularly if the antenna is quite long. In that case, use a truss from the vertical support, as shown. Possible materials for the truss include nylon or polypropylene rope. Poly is superior because it stretches less. Eye bolts are shown for supporting the truss line. Both booms require support, but only one truss is shown. The antenna's horizontal supports may be attached to the vertical mast with U-bolts. If the mast does not make contact with the helix, you might be able to use a metal mast, but I recommend plastic or wood.

There is one discouraging fact. Polarization is not standardized. I suggest that you make the antenna with right-hand sense, i.e., spiraling clockwise like the thread of a screw or a waiter's corkscrew. This is most likely to work well, but if the station you want uses left-hand polarization, or if a reflected signal is superior to a direct signal, you'll have to build another antenna with left-hand sense.

As with all outdoor antennas, use a grounding block to prevent damage from lightning strikes. In this case, a lightning rod atop the antenna, separately grounded with a heavy gauge wire that is run behind the ground screen, won't hurt either. If you use a metal mast, make sure it is grounded.

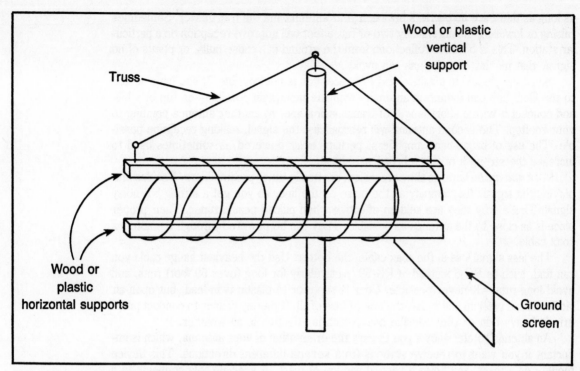

Fig. 11-12. Construction of a helical antenna.

GENERAL TIPS ON ANTENNAS AND RECEPTION

"You can't be too rich or too thin," a movie star once said. If you're an antenna, you can't be too high to receive distant stations. The usual reception range for an FM station is 40 to 50 miles. Beyond that point, stereo is impossible, monophonic reception is noisy, and adjacent station interference begins to get in the way. Yet when I visited a friend on the island of Hawaii, he received FM and TV stations from Honolulu, 300 miles away. Of course, most of that distance was over open ocean, and his home was on the side of a volcano, 3000 feet above sea level. He claimed that on a clear night, he could see the lights of Honolulu. Reception from Hilo, less than 50 miles away, but over another 8000 feet of mountain, was impossible. If you can mount your antenna 3000 feet high, with a line-of-sight path to the transmitter, you too might receive stations 300 or more miles away.

Doubling the height of your antenna will increase its range of by 50%. Under rare conditions, VHF radio waves such as FM and TV transmissions will be reflected by clouds and thermal layers. Sometimes such air layers will form a tunnel with the ocean surface, channeling FM and TV signals over the Atlantic. In late summer, European stations can sometimes be picked up in New England this way. But for the most part, FM reception is line-of-sight, and limited by the horizon. To get more distant stations, you will have to raise your antenna.

Most people can't put a 3000-foot tower in their yard, but if the antenna is at least 1.5 wavelengths high, (15 feet for FM) reception will be good out to the 50-mile range

159

as long as there are no barriers between your antenna and the transmitter. Sometimes raising or lowering the antenna by two or three feet will improve reception on a particular station. This is because reflections from the ground can cause nulls, or points of no signal, that moving the antenna can avoid.

Some people live in a valley, and FM reception is not possible. If you have access to the land, you can mount an antenna—with the most gain possible—on top of a hill, and connect it with a short length of transmission line, to another antenna pointing to your rooftop. The second antenna will rebroadcast the signal, making reception possible. The use of broad-band amplifiers, perhaps solar powered, is sometimes used to increase the strength of the rebroadcast signal.

Antenna amplifiers, as they are called, are really tuner preamplifiers. Besides amplifying the signal, they amplify all the noise on the line, so you get a strong but noisy signal. That's why they are seldom effective when placed near a tuner. Their proper place is as close to the antenna as possible. They can be powered through the antenna coax cable.

The less signal loss in the coax cable, the better. Use the heaviest gauge cable you can find, such as RG-6 instead of RG-59, particularly for long (over 50 foot) runs, and avoid long runs whenever possible. Coax is superior to plastic twin-lead, but open-air ladder line, if you can find it, has the lowest loss of all. It merely ceases to conduct properly in heavy rain or snow, unlike coax,which is effective in all weather.

An antenna rotator allows you to vary the orientation of your antenna, which is important if you want to receive stations from several different directions. This device mounts on a mast, and holds a second section of mast. A special cable connects to a control box in your house, which allows you to turn your antenna as you tune your receiver. These devices start at about $60. More expensive models have stronger bearings to take more weight, so you can turn a larger antenna or antenna array. The best models have physical stops, which will prevent the wind from turning the antenna when you aren't adjusting it.

You can buy very good FM antennas, which are superior for FM reception to TV-FM combinations. Radio Shack's best model (#15-1636) has about 14 dB gain. If you want better reception than your TV antenna provides, try this model or a similar one. All such antennas are based on a broad-band log-periodic dipole design, so they are effective across the entire FM band. Prices are low enough so that it is not worth building one yourself.

If mounted too close together, (less than five feet) antennas interfere with each other. If your antenna shares the mast with another, make sure they are five feet or more apart vertically. If there is another antenna mast on the rooftop, make sure it isn't between your antenna and the transmitter. If it is, raise, lower, or move one of them.

Two identical antennas, mounted one over the other, can double reception power. The best spacing for stacked antennas is one wavelength (ten feet for FM), but half that (five feet) gives acceptable results. Five-eighths of a wavelength (six feet) is much better than five feet. The difference between six and ten feet might not be worth the extra construction effort. The antennas will have to be connected in phase. Coax lines of equal length should be fed from the antennas to a signal-combiner (Radio Shack #15-1141), which will maintain the proper impedances. Horizontal combinations are also possible, maintaining a six-foot (⅝ wavelength) spacing between the nearest elements of either antenna. A four-antenna array consisting of two vertical stacks side by side will have six-dB gain over a single antenna. Perhaps the practical limitation is the structure necessary to mount the array.

If you want to use circular polarization for any matching pair of commercial outdoor antennas, it can be done. The antennas must be mounted perpendicular to each other so that they are cross polarized. The 75-ohm coax lines coming from each antenna must be fed to a signal-combiner (Radio Shack #15-1141) to match two 75-ohm lines to one 75-ohm line; length of the lines is not critical, but one must be an electrical quarter-wave longer than the other. (21-⅜ inches at 98 MHz.) Polarization sense can be changed by interchanging the lines at the combiner that run from the combiner to the antennas. Perhaps the biggest problem with this kind of setup is physically mounting the antennas. Construction is easier if the antennas are close to each other; because they are mounted at right angles, one vertical, one horizontal, they do not interfere with each other the way two stacked antennas would. This makes it possible to mount them on the same mast. Some attempt to weather-proof the combiner and also associated connectors should be made, such as enclosing it in a plastic case or covering it with silicone sealer, then wrapping with water-proof plastic tape.

When you are putting up your antenna, exercise extreme caution around power lines. If you're holding a metal boom when it comes in contact with a power line, you will probably be electrocuted. Falls from rooftops are another hazard. Unless the roof is flat, safety lines like a mountain climber's aren't a bad idea.

Antennas make good lightning rods. If the ground path is through your tuner, you won't have a tuner. If the tuner catches fire, your house could burn, and then you won't have a house, either. A grounding block for the antenna line is a must. The mast on which the antenna is mounted should be separately grounded with a heavy copper line to a metal stake driven a couple of feet into the ground. If there are higher structures nearby, you might think this precaution unnecessary. But lightning doesn't always strike the highest point; the best ground path is what it will follow, and that might be your antenna. Make sure that if it does strike, the path to ground is direct and avoids your equipment.

REFERENCES

Staff of the American Radio Relay League. *The Radio Amateur's Handbook*. Newington, CT: The American Radio Relay League, Inc., (updated yearly).

Hall, Gerald L. (Ed.). *The ARRL Antenna Book*. Newington, CT: The American Radio Relay League, Inc., (updated yearly).

Orr, William I. *Radio Handbook*, 22nd ed. Indianapolis, IN: Howard W. Sams & CO., Inc., 1981.

Appendix:
Parts Sources and Parts Lists for Projects

FINDING PARTS HAS BECOME DIFFICULT FOR THE ELECTRONICS HOBBYIST. RADIO SHACK is the onlyhobbyist. Radio Shack is the only store where most people can buy parts wholesale. Their prices are usually decent, but they don't carry everything.

One way to locate parts sources (and kits) is to look through the advertisements in the back pages of the electronics hobby magazines, such as *Radio Electronics* and *Modern Electronics*. The classified ad pages in *Audio* are a good source for companies that supply speakers, as well as "audiophile" capacitors. Send away for as many catalogs as possible. Companies go in and out of business; the players are always changing. I am not including a more complete list of suppliers for fear that it will be obsolete by the time it is read. The following are some of the sources I have used recently.

All Electronics
905 S. Vermont Ave., PO Box 20406
Los Angeles, CA 90006

All Electronics is the least expensive source I have found for large electrolytic capacitors suitable for amplifier power supplies. They specialize in surplus parts. If they have what you need, chances are it's at a bargain price.

Mark V Electronics
PO Box 6610
Alhambra, CA 91802
1-818-282-1196

Mark V is the exclusive U.S. distributer for Tung Yung and Sound Master, two Hong Kong kit manufacturers. They carry amplifiers, preamps, and accessories. Though instructions are not always translated into proper English, I have found them understandable. They also carry black rack-mountable cases for projects, as well as transformers for all their kits. Their catalog costs only $1.

Rivera
660 Amsterdam Ave Dept. 131
New York, NY 10025

Rivera carries all values of resistors, potentiometers, and capacitors mentioned in this book, at the lowest possible prices. They have developed a series of "stuffing guides" for every project, showing how to mount the parts on a Radio Shack IC board. (But they can't top Radio Shack's prices for boards.) No minimum order, but $1 handling charge for orders under $5. Their catalog is $1.

Meniscus
3275 Gladiola Ave.
Wyoming, MI 49509
1-616-534-9121

Madisound Speaker Components
8982 Table Bluff Rd.
Box 4283
Madison, Wisconsin 53711
1-608-767-2673

Speakerlab, unfortunately, no longer sells its drivers, preferring to concentrate its business on finished speaker systems. Both of these companies carry quality drivers. Their catalogs are free.

Index

Index

Other Bestsellers From TAB

☐ **HOW TO BUILD A SMALL BUDGET RECORDING STUDIO FROM SCRATCH . . . WITH 12 TEST DESIGNS—2nd Edition—F. Alton Everest and Mike Shea**

Studios that offer function and economy as well as good sound quality. This unique volume is an authoritative, non-mathematical approach to planning and building those small acoustics studios. Containing all the current background data you need to design, construct, and operate your own budget recording studio, this book will shed light on the obscure and intangible science of sound. With 12 proven plans for acoustical studios, authors Everest and Shea show how YOU can produce audio, radio, film, and television program material. 306 pp., Fully Illustrated.

Paper $17.95   Hard $22.95
Book No. 2966

☐ **AMPLIFIERS SIMPLIFIED, with 40 Projects—Delton T. Horn**

At last! A book on amplifiers that actually tells you what devices are used in which types of applications. Horn leads you through proper use of transistors, FETs, op-amps, and other DIP packages. He explains basic theory and covers problems commonly associated with amplifiers, plus, 40 carefully selected projects provide hands-on experience in working with various types of amplifiers. 208 pp., 129 illus.

Paper $13.95   Hard $16.95
Book No. 2885

☐ **TROUBLESHOOTING AND REPAIRING AUDIO EQUIPMENT—Homer L. Davidson**

When your telephone answering machine quits . . . when your cassette player grinds to a stop . . . when your TV remote loses control . . . or when your compact disc player goes berserk . . . You don't need a degree in electronics or even any experience. Everything you need to troubleshoot and repair most common problems in almost any consumer audio equipment is here in a servicing guide that's guaranteed to save you time and money! 336 pp., 354 illus.

Paper $18.95   Hard $24.95
Book No. 2867

☐ **ELECTROSTATIC LOUDSPEAKER DESIGN AND CONSTRUCTION—Ronald Wagner**

This one-of-a-kind guide demonstrates, step-by-step, how you can design and build your own commercial quality electrostatic loudspeakers for hundreds of dollars less than the retail price! And it's easier than you might think! The easy-to-follow, clear instructions make this seemingly ambitious project suitable not only for the advanced electronics hobbyist but also for audio amateurs. Covers both the theory of electrostatic loudspeakers and the practical techniques used in building one. 256 pp., 178 illus.

Paper $16.95   Hard $23.95
Book No. 2832

☐ **DIGITAL ELECTRONIC MUSIC SYNTHESIZERS—2nd Edition—Delton T. Horn**

Digital and analog components, and interfacing standards, are examined in relation to music synthesis, and digitally generating and manipulating sounds are discussed. Covered are commercial units by Yamaha, Casio, Siel, Oberheim, Kawai, Wersi, and others. Plus, Horn includes a section on building your own synthesizer. Projects include keyboards, an op amp organ, digital poly-syngan, modulators, and drones. 256 pp., 140 illus.

Paper $16.95   Hard $21.95
Book No. 2695

☐ **CREATIVE SOUND RECORDING ON A BUDGET—Delton T. Horn**

Here's where you'll find exactly what it takes to make recordings you can really be proud of—whether you're recording musical groups, mixing, dubbing, taping live drama, or almost any other recording situation you can think of! It's an invaluable sourcebook filled with practical tips and techniques for getting professional-quality sound from inexpensive recording equipment! Horn covers basic recording methods as well as all kinds of special effects enhanced by plenty of suggestions on how to adapt them to suit your own individual requirements. He gives you advice on choosing equipment along with care and maintenance hints. He also shows how you can build your own home studio *without going broke*, provides details on sound-proofing and minimizing room effects on your sound, and even covers live location recording. 224 pp., 140 illus.

Paper $11.95   Hard $19.95
Book No. 2635

☐ **SUCCESSFUL SOUND SYSTEM OPERATION—F. Alton Everest**

Here's an invaluable guide, written by a professional acoustics consultant and audio engineer, that focuses on how you can effectively coordinate every component in your sound system for maximum performance. Including a full explanation of how sound systems work, it features advice on equipment usage, plus tips on troubleshooting and repairing audio equipment. 336 pp., 321 illus.

Paper $14.95   Book No. 2606

☐ **AUDIO SWEETENING FOR FILM AND TV—Hubatka, Hull, and Sanders**

Contains the information you need to create high quality audio for film and video productions. It provides complete instructions for producers who want to improve video tracks, and experienced audio engineers who want to learn video editing techniques! Shows how to create sound tracks using high quality recorders, monitors, amplifiers, mixing consoles, and synchronizers. 240 pp., 99 illus., 6″ x 9″.

Hard $30.00   Book No. 1994